EDITH WHARTON'S *ETHAN FROME:*
The Story with Sources and Commentary

**SCRIBNER
RESEARCH
ANTHOLOGIES**

Martin Steinmann, Jr., GENERAL EDITOR

BLAKE NEVIUS
The University of California, Los Angeles

EDITH WHARTON'S *ETHAN FROME:*
The Story with Sources and Commentary

SCRIBNER
RESEARCH
ANTHOLOGIES

CHARLES SCRIBNER'S SONS   New York

Preface

Each Scribner Research Anthology is a collection of written sources upon a single historical, political, literary, or scientific topic or problem—the Hungarian Revolt, Shakespeare's *Julius Cæsar,* or extrasensory perception, for example. In addition to these sources, it contains (1) "Guide to Research," an account of the rationale and the methods of research and of research-paper writing, (2) an introduction to the topic of the anthology, (3) suggested topics for controlled research, and (4) suggested sources and topics for library research.

Each anthology is designed to serve two purposes. First, each gives the student access to important sources—texts, documents, letters, diaries, essays, articles, reports, transcripts of hearings, for instance—on a given topic. Some of these sources are otherwise available in only a few libraries, some (manuscripts and historical and government documents) in only one. In any case, the collection as a whole is not otherwise available in one volume. Second, each anthology gives the student either all his sources for a controlled-research paper or some of them for a library-research paper. Each anthology can be valuable either for readings in courses in history, literature, science, or humanities or as the basis for a research paper in these or in other courses.

A controlled-research paper—a paper in which the student's search for sources is limited to, and in certain ways controlled by, those sources contained in one anthology—is not so noble an undertaking as a library-research paper. But it is often more successful—more rewarding for the student and easier for his instructor to teach effectively and judge fairly. Its advantages for both student and instructor are often considerable.

For the student, it sometimes provides sources unavailable in his school library. And it enables him to learn a good deal about research (selection, interpretation, and evaluation of sources; quotation and paraphrase; and documentation) without prior instruction in use of the library (and, incidentally, without overtaxing the facilities and the resources of his library and without loss of, or damage to, sources either irreplaceable or difficult and expensive to replace).

For the instructor, it permits focus of class discussion upon a limited set of topics. It enables him to track down the student's sources conveniently. And—perhaps the greatest advantage of all—it enables him to judge both conveniently and exactly how well the student has selected, interpreted, and evaluated his sources and how well he has quoted and paraphrased them.

In many schools, a controlled-research paper is either a preliminary to or a part of a library-research paper. A library-research paper is probably the most difficult paper that the student can be assigned to write. The problems that confront him are not simply those common to any paper—organization, paragraphing, and transitions, for instance—and those (already mentioned) common to all research papers. He has, in addition, the problem of using the library well—of, for example, using the card catalogue, periodical indexes, and other reference works. But, if the instructor assigns a controlled-research paper as a preliminary to or, as it were, an early part of a library-research paper, the student need not come to grips with all these problems at once.

Each Scribner Research Anthology is compiled according to the following editorial principles. Each source that is not anonymous is prefaced by a biographical note on its author. At the foot of the same page is a bibliographical note. Each source is reprinted exactly as it appears in the original except for (1) some typographical peculiarities, (2) explanatory notes, given in brackets, and (3) omissions, indicated by ellipses (". . ."). And, finally, for each source that has pagination in the original, page numbers are given in brackets within the source itself—thus: "[**320/321**]," where everything before the slash (and after the preceding slash, if any) is from page 320, and everything after the slash (and before the next slash, if any) is from page 321. For a source hitherto unpublished, no page numbers are given; and the student who uses it should cite the page numbers of the Scribner Research Anthology. Footnotes to a source are given as in the original. Where the original pagination of a footnote is not evident, its page number precedes it in brackets.

MARTIN STEINMANN, JR.

Bingham Bay
Lake Gogebic
August, 1960

Guide to Research

THE IDEA OF RESEARCH

Research is the organized, disciplined search for truth; the aim of all research is to discover the truth about something. That thing may be a historical object like the Stonehenge monuments or a historical event like the Hungarian Revolt or the Battle of Waterloo. It may be a work of literature like Shakespeare's *Julius Cæsar* or Miller's *Death of a Salesman*. It may be a recurring event like the motions of the planets or the circulation of the blood. It may be an experimentally repeatable phenomenon like behavior of rats in a maze or perception apparently unaccounted for by the five senses. Or it may be a political problem like the decision to use the atomic bomb in World War II. Archeology, history, political science, literary criticism and scholarship, astronomy, physiology, and psychology—these are some of the many divisions of research. Indeed, all the sciences—physical, biological, and social—and all other scholarly disciplines share this organized, disciplined search for truth.

The search for truth has often been confused with such aims as confirming prejudice, instilling patriotism, and praising friends and blaming enemies. The attempt to prove the preconceived conclusion *that* one college is superior to another, for example, is not research (though the attempt to discover *whether* one college is so superior is). Research is hostile to prejudice.

General Methods of Research. The best general method of research is first-hand observation. But this method is not always possible and, when it is possible, not always practical.

The best method to begin discovering the truth about something is to observe that thing and the circumstances surrounding it. To discover the truth about *Julius Cæsar* or *Death of a Salesman*, get the play and read it, or go to the theatre and watch a performance. To discover the truth about the planets, observe them through your telescope. To discover the truth about the intelligence of rats, build a maze and run some rats through it.

This first-hand observation is not always possible, however. To discover the truth about the Battle of Waterloo, you can't observe the battle. The best that you or anyone else can do is to observe other persons' observations, the recorded observations of eye-witnesses: diaries, letters, and memoirs, for instance, of soldiers and generals who were in the battle. With more recent historical events—for example, the Hungarian Revolt—you are better off. You can watch films and listen to tape recordings. You may be able to interview people who were there. But these observations are still second-hand; and, on the whole, history can be observed only at second-hand. The sole exception is history that you have been part of. You may have fought in the Hungarian Revolt—though, if you did, you may be prejudiced.

Even when first-hand observation is possible, it is not always practical. You may have a copy of or tickets to *Julius Cæsar* or *Death of a Salesman* but not know enough about the principles of dramatic criticism to interpret the play unaided. You may have a telescope but not know how to use it or, if you do, not know what to make of what you observe through it. You may have some rats but not know how to build a maze or, if you do, not know enough about animal psychology to run your rats through it properly. The best that *you* can do under these circumstances is to supplement whatever first-hand observations you can make with observations of the first-hand observations of other people better-trained or better-equipped than you. Read *Julius Cæsar* or *Death of a Salesman* and also critics' interpretations of the play. Observe the planets, if you can, and read treatises on astronomy. Do what you can with your rats, and read reports of experiments with rats. After all, no one can master the special methods and come by the special equipment of all scholarly disciplines. Indeed, few people can do this with more than one discipline, and then not before they're thirty. But all people who want a liberal education should try to discover as much of the truth about as many scholarly disciplines as their abilities and their circumstances permit. Indeed, the achievement of this is what is meant by "a liberal education."

Primary and Secondary Sources. As the foregoing account of the general methods of research suggests, there is, ultimately, only one source of the truth about something—the thing, the event, or the phenomenon itself: the Stonehenge monuments, the Hungarian Revolt, or the Battle of Waterloo; the text of *Julius Cæsar* or *Death of a Salesman;* Robert Oppenheimer's testimony on the use of the atomic bomb against Japan; the motions of the planets or the circulation of blood; extrasensory perceptions or rats running in a maze. Such a source is a *primary* source. And, in historical research, where the thing itself (the Hungarian Revolt or the Battle of Waterloo) cannot be observed at first hand, a report of an eyewitness or a film or a tape recording is also counted as a *primary* source. But any other second-hand source (an interpretation of *Julius Cæsar* or *Death of a Salesman,* a treatise on astronomy, a report of an experiment with rats) is a *secondary* source.

A primary source is, of course, better. But, if a primary source is unavailable to you (if it is a book, perhaps your school library does not have it) or if you are not trained or equipped to use it (you don't know how to run rats through a maze or you have no telescope), then a secondary source must do. In any case, except for the most mature scientists and scholars, a good

secondary source is useful and often indispensable.

It is worth noticing that being primary or being secondary is not an intrinsic characteristic of the source itself. It is, rather, a relationship that either exists or does not exist between a given source and a given topic of research. Consequently, a given source may be primary in relation to one given topic but secondary in relation to another. Two examples may serve to make this important point clear. Edward Gibbon's *The Decline and Fall of the Roman Empire* (1776–1788) is a secondary source in relation to the topic of the Roman Empire but a primary source in relation to that of eighteenth-century English prose style or that of eighteenth-century historiography. Samuel Taylor Coleridge's *Lectures on Shakespeare* (1811–1812) is a secondary source in relation to the topic of Shakespeare's plays but a primary source in relation to that of nineteenth-century principles of dramatic criticism or that of Shakespeare's reputation.

It is worth noticing also that a given source may be primary or secondary in relationship to more than one topic. James Joyce's novel *A Portrait of the Artist as a Young Man* is a primary source in relation not only to the topic of the structure of *A Portrait of the Artist as a Young Man* (and dozens of other topics on the novel itself) but also to the topic of use of the stream-of-consciousness technique in twentieth-century fiction.

THE RESEARCH PAPER

A research paper is a paper giving the results of research, the methods by which they were reached, and the sources, primary or secondary, which were used. A research paper attempts to tell the truth about a topic, and also tells how and where this truth was discovered. As we have seen, the sources of a research paper may be either written sources (literary texts and historical documents, for example) or sources of other kinds (experiments, for example). Since a research paper written in school is almost always based upon written (printed) sources, we shall here discuss only that kind. A research paper based upon written sources may be either a library-research paper or a controlled-research paper. A library-research paper is a research paper for which your search for sources is limited to those sources contained in the libraries available to you; a controlled-research paper, to those sources contained in one anthology —to those contained in this volume, for example. Here we shall emphasize the latter kind.

Finding Your Topic. The first step in writing a research paper based upon written sources, whether a library-research or a controlled-research paper, is finding a topic. We say "finding a topic" rather than "choosing a topic" because the process is more like finding a job than choosing a sandwich from a menu. Unless your instructor assigns you a topic, which he may do, you must look for one; and the one you find may not be just what you want but the best one that you can find. But, if you look long and carefully, you may find a topic that so well suits your interests, your capacities, and the time and the space at your disposal that your paper will almost surely be a success.

Finding a topic is the most important single step in writing a research paper, and the things that you should have in mind when looking for a topic are (1) your interests, (2) your capacities, and (3) the time and the space at your disposal. If you are interested in a topic, if you know something about the special methods of research that the topic requires, and if your topic is narrow enough to require no more time than you have for research and no greater development than you can give it in a paper of the length assigned you, then the paper that results will probably be satisfactory. For example, the topic of figures of speech in *Julius Cæsar* may interest you greatly. But, if it does, you must ask yourself whether you know enough about figures of speech to do research on them

and, if you do, whether this topic is narrow enough. Even the topic of metaphors in the play would be too broad for most papers; metaphors in Brutus' soliloquies might be about right. In any case, before you take a topic for a paper, you should do some reading on that topic; otherwise, you won't know whether it is interesting, within your ability to handle, and within the scope of your assigned paper.

Once you think that you've found a topic, take great care in phrasing it. The best phrasing is a question or a series of closely related questions. Better than "The character of Brutus" is "To what extent is Brutus motivated by self-interest and to what extent by the public interest?" The latter is not only more narrow and more precise; it provides you with a criterion of relevance in selecting your sources. At the end of this volume, you will find a list of suggested topics, intended to call your attention to topics that might not occur to you. But these topics are suggestive rather than definitive or precise.

Finding Your Sources. Finding sources for a library-research paper and finding ones for a controlled-research paper, though different in several respects, are alike in certain others. Finding sources in the library requires knowledge of how to use the card catalogue, periodical indexes, special bibliographies, reserve shelves, and encyclopedias. Finding sources in this volume or a similar one does not. But, in either case, you must have a clear idea of what you are looking for; and you must be prepared to put up with a high ratio of looking to finding. In other words, you must have not only criteria of relevance but also a willingness to do a good deal of skimming and a good deal more of careful reading, some of it fruitless.

The basic criterion of relevance you provide by careful phrasing of your topic, a problem discussed in the preceding section. The other criteria you provide by making a preliminary or tentative outline —perhaps in the form of subtopics, perhaps in the form of questions. Such an outline is not to be used for your paper. The outline for your paper will probably be quite different and, in any event, cannot be made until after you find your sources and take your notes. This preliminary outline guides your research and, as we shall see, provides you with the subtopic headings necessary for your note-cards (see "Taking Your Notes," page xi) .

Making Your Working Bibliography. Once you have found a promising source ("promising" because, though it seems to be relevant, it may turn out not to be) you want to make some record of it so that, once you have completed your search for sources, you can turn back to it, read it, and, if it turns out to be relevant, take notes on it. This record of promising sources is your *working* bibliography. It is so called for two reasons: first, because you work with it as you proceed with your research and the writing of your paper, adding promising sources to it and discarding irrelevant ones; and, second, because this designation distinguishes it from your final bibliography, which appears at the very end of your research paper and contains only sources actually used in the paper. For a controlled-research paper, your working bibliography may be nothing more elaborate than a series of check marks in the table of contents of your research anthology or a list of page numbers. For a library-research paper, however, you need something quite different.

A working bibliography for a library-research paper is a collection of three-by-five cards each representing a promising source and each containing full information about that source. Once you have completed your research, written your paper, and discarded all promising but (as they turned out) irrelevant sources, this bibliography is identical with your final bibliography. Having a separate card for each source enables you to add and to discard sources easily and to sort and arrange them easily in any order you please. Eventually, when this bibliography becomes identical with your final bibliography, you will arrange sources alphabetically by au-

thors' last names. Having full information about each source on its card enables you to turn back to it easily—to locate it in the library without first looking it up again. You find this information in the card catalogue, periodical indexes, or other bibliographical aids; or, when browsing through the shelves or the stacks of the library and coming upon a promising source, you find it in or on the source itself—for example, on the spine and the title page of a book.

If the source is a *book,* you should put the following information on the three-by-five working-bibliography card:
(1) the library call number,
(2) the author's (or authors') full name (or names), last name first for the first author,
(3) the title of the book,
(4) the name of the city of publication,
(5) the name of the publisher (*not* the printer), and
(6) the year of publication (often found on the other side of the title page).
See the example of such a card on the opposite page (note the punctuation carefully).

If the source is a *periodical article,* you should put the following information on the three-by-five working-bibliography card:
(1) the author's (or authors') full name (or names),
(2) the title of the article,
(3) the name of the periodical,
(4) the volume number,
(5) the week, the month, or the season of publication, together with the year, and
(6) the page numbers covered by the article.
See the example of such a card on the opposite page (note the punctuation carefully).

These two forms take care of the two standard cases. For special cases—such things as books with editors or translators as well as authors, books published in several editions or in several volumes, and daily newspapers—see any good handbook of composition.

860.3
J23

Jones, John A., and William C. Brown. <u>A History of Serbia</u>. New York: The Rowland Press, Inc., 1934.

WORKING-BIBLIOGRAPHY CARD FOR A BOOK

Smith, Harold B. "Fishing in Serbian Waters." <u>Journal of Balkan Sports</u>, VII (May 1936), 26-32.

WORKING-BIBLIOGRAPHY CARD FOR A PERIODICAL ARTICLE

Taking Your Notes. Once you have found sources, entered them in your working bibliography, read them, and found them relevant, taking notes requires your exactly following a standard procedure if your notes are going to be useful to you when you come to write your paper. An extra five minutes given to taking a note correctly can save you a half hour in writing your paper. Here is the standard procedure:

(1) Take all notes on four-by-six cards. Never use notebooks, loose sheets of paper, or backs of old envelopes.

(2) Limit each note to information on a single subtopic of your preliminary outline *and* from a single source. It follows from this that you may have many cards on the same subtopic and many cards from the same source but that you may never have one card on more than one subtopic or from more than one source.

(3) On each card, in addition to the note itself, put

  (a) the appropriate subtopic heading in the upper left-hand corner,

  (b) the name of the source (usually the author's last name will do) in the upper right-hand corner, and

  (c) the page number (or numbers) of that part (or those parts) of the source that you have used in taking your note. If you have used more than one page, indicate your page numbers in such a way that, when you come to write your paper, you can tell what page each part of the note comes from, for you may not use the whole note. (If you follow these first three rules, you will be able, when you come to outline and to organize your paper, to sort your notes in any way you please—by subtopic, for example—and to arrange them in any order you please. Such flexibility is impossible if you take your notes in a notebook. If you follow the third rule, you will also be able to document your paper —write footnotes, for example—without again referring to the sources themselves.)

(4) In taking the note itself, paraphrase or quote your source or do both; but do only one at a time, and use quotation very sparingly.

Paraphrase and quotation require special care. Anything between paraphrase and quotation is not acceptable to good writers: you either paraphrase or quote, but do nothing in between. To paraphrase a source (or part of a source) is to reproduce it in words and word orders substantially different from the original. When you paraphrase well, you keep the sense of the original but change the language, retaining some key words, of course, but otherwise using your own words and your own sentence patterns. To quote a source (or part of a source) is to reproduce it exactly. When you quote well, you keep both the sense and the language of the original, retaining its punctuation, its capitalization, its type face (roman or italic), and its spelling (indeed, even its misspelling).

Omissions and additions require special care. If, when quoting, you wish to omit some of the original, you may do so only if the omission does not change the sense of the original (never leave out a "not," for example!) *and* if it is indicated by ellipses (three spaced periods: ". . ."). If you wish to add something to the original, you may do so only if the addition does not change the sense of the original (never add a "not"!) *and* it is indicated by square brackets. The most usual additions are explanations ("They [i.e., the people of Paris] were alarmed") and disclaimers of errors in the original, indicated by the Latin *"sic,"* meaning "thus" (Colombis [*sic*] discovered America in 1592 [*sic*]"). You must, of course, carry these ellipses and square brackets from your note-cards to your paper. And, if you type your paper, brackets may be a problem, for most typewriter keyboards do not include them. If your keyboard does not, you may do one of two things—either use the slash ("/") and underlining ("__" and "—") in such a way as to produce a bracket ("⌐" and "⌐") or draw brackets in with a pen. In any event, don't substitute parentheses for brackets.

In your paper, quotations no longer than three or four lines are to be enclosed within a set of quotation marks and run into your text; longer ones are to be set off from the text, without quotation marks, by indention from the left-hand margin and, especially in typewritten copy, by single-spacing. But never use either of these devices unless the language is exactly that of the original.

Your usual treatment of a source should be paraphrase; use quotation only if the

Fly - fishing   Smith
   Smith says that fly-fishing is a
method of fishing used chiefly by
wealthy Serbians and foreign tourists,
that the flies used are generally imported
from Scotland, and that "Serbian trout
are so snobbish that they won't glance [27/28]
at a domestic fly."
   [Query: How reliable is the information
in this rather facetious article?]

NOTE-CARD

language of the original is striking (strikingly good or strikingly bad), if it is the very topic of your research (as in a paper on Shakespeare's style), or if it is so complex (as it might be in a legal document) that you don't want to risk paraphrasing it.

Let us look at the sample note-card above. The topic of research is methods of fishing in Serbia; the subtopic that the note deals with is fly-fishing in Serbia; the source is Harold B. Smith's article "Fishing in Serbian Waters," from the *Journal of Balkan Sports* (see the second of the two working-bibliography cards on page xi).

Note the subtopic heading ("Fly-fishing") in the upper left-hand corner; the name of the source, abbreviated to the author's last name ("Smith"), in the upper right-hand corner; the page numbers ("[27/28]"), indicating that everything, both paraphrase and quotation, up through the word "glance" is from page 27 and that everything after that word is from page 28; the sparing and appropriate use of quotation; and the bracketed query, to remind the note-taker that he must use this source with caution.

Writing Your Paper. Many of the problems of writing a research paper based upon written sources—organization, the outline, the thesis paragraph, topic sentences, transitions, and the like—are problems of expository writing generally. Here we shall discuss only those problems peculiar to such a paper. Two of these problems—paraphrase and quotation— we discussed in the preceding section. Two others remain: reaching conclusions and avoiding the scissors-and-paste organization.

When you come to make the outline for your paper and to write your paper, you will have before you three things:

(1) your *preliminary* outline, containing ordered subtopics of your topic; (2) your working bibliography; and (3) your note-cards. These are the *immediate* results of your research; they are not the *final* results. They are only the raw material out of which you must fashion your paper. At best, they are an intermediate stage between finding your topic and making your final outline. The preliminary outline will not do for the final outline. The working bibliography will almost certainly require further pruning. And the note-cards will require sorting, evaluation, organization, pruning, and exercise of logic and common sense. All this needs to be done, preferably before you make your final outline and begin to write your paper, though almost inevitably some of it will remain to bedevil you while you are writing it. To put the matter in another way, you are, with these things before you, a Sherlock Holmes who has gathered all his clues but who has reached no conclusions from them, who has not come to the end of his search for truth. You must discard irrelevant clues, ones that have no bearing on the questions that you want answered. You must arbitrate the claims of conflicting or contradictory clues. You must decide which one of several probable conclusions is the most probable.

Once you have reached your conclusions, you must organize your paper and set forth this organization in your final outline. Organization and the outline are, of course, problems common to all expository writing. But a problem peculiar to the research paper is avoiding the scissors-and-paste organization—avoiding a paper that looks as though you had cut paraphrases and quotations out of your note-cards, pasted them in columns on paper, and connected them only with such phrases as "Jones says" and "On the other hand, Brown says." Such an organization is the result of a failure to reach conclusions (with the consequence that there is nothing but "Jones says" to put in between paraphrases and quotations);

or it is a failure to see the necessity of giving the conclusions reached *and* the reasoning by which they were reached (with the consequence that, though there is something to put between paraphrases and quotations, nothing is put there, and the reader is left to write the paper for himself).

Documenting Your Paper. To document your paper is to give the source of each paraphrase and quotation that it contains, so that your reader can, if he wishes to, check each of your sources and judge for himself what use you have made of it. To give the source is usually to give (1) either the information that you have about that source in your working bibliography (except that the name of the publisher of a book is usually not given) or the information that accompanies each source in a research anthology *and* (2) the information about page numbers that you have in your notes. This information you may give either formally or informally, as your instructor decides.

Formal documentation is given in footnotes. For a full discussion of footnotes, see any good handbook (one cheap and widely accepted one is *The MLA Style Sheet*). The form of footnotes is similar to, but not identical with, the form of bibliographical entries. With these three sample footnotes, compare the two sample working-bibliography cards on page xi:

[1] John A. Jones and William C. Brown, *A History of Serbia* (New York, 1934), p. 211.
[2] Harold B. Smith, "Fishing in Serbian Waters," *Journal of Balkan Sports*, VII (May 1936), 27.
[3] Smith, pp. 27-28.

Informal documentation is given in the text of the paper, usually parenthetically, as in this example:

> Fly-fishing in Serbia is chiefly a sport of wealthy Serbians and foreign tourists (Harold B. Smith, "Fishing in Serbian Waters," *Journal of Balkan Sports*, VII [May 1936], 27), though in some mountain districts it is popular among the peasants (John A. Jones and William C. Brown, *A History of Serbia*

[New York, 1934], p. 211). The flies used are generally imported from Scotland; indeed, Smith facetiously adds, "Serbian trout are so snobbish that they won't glance at a domestic fly" (pp. 27-28).

As this example suggests, however, informal documentation can be an annoying distraction. It probably works out best in papers that use only a few sources. In such papers, there are few occasions for long first-references to sources: for example, "(Harold B. Smith, "Fishing in Serbian Waters," *Journal of Balkan Sports,* VII [May 1936], 27)." But there are many occasions for short succeeding-references: for example, "(Smith, pp. 27-28)" or "(pp. 27-28)." Occasionally, informal documentation may be profitably combined with formal, as in a paper about Shakespeare's *Julius Cæsar.* In such a paper, references to the play might well be given informally—for example, "(III.ii.2-7)"—but references to critics formally.

How many footnotes (or parenthetical documentations) do you need in your paper? The answer is, of course, that you need as many footnotes as you have paraphrases or quotations of sources, unless you group several paraphrases or quotations *from the same page or consecutive pages of a given source* in such a way that one footnote will do for all. One way to do this grouping—almost the only way— is to introduce the group with such a sentence as "Smith's views on fly-fishing are quite different from Brown's" and to con-

clude it with the raised numeral referring to the footnote. Your reader will understand that everything between the introductory sentence and the numeral comes from the page or the successive pages of the source indicated in the footnote.

Making Your Final Bibliography. Your paper concludes with your final bibliography, which is simply a list of all the sources—and only those sources—that you actually paraphrase or quote in your paper. In other words, every source that you give in a footnote (or a parenthetical documentation) you include in your final bibliography; and you include no other sources (inclusion of others results in what is unfavorably known as "a padded bibliography"). The form for entries in your final bibliography is identical with that for ones in your working bibliography, given above. You should list these sources alphabetically by authors' last names or, if a source is anonymous, by the first word of its title, but not by "a," "an," or "the." For example:

BIBLIOGRAPHY

Jones, John A., and William C. Brown. *A History of Serbia.* New York: The Rowland Press, Inc., 1934.
"Serbian Pastimes." *Sports Gazette,* XCI (October 26, 1952), 18-19, 38, 40-42.
Smith, Harold B. "Fishing in Serbian Waters," *Journal of Balkan Sports,* VII (May 1936), 26-32.

MARTIN STEINMANN, JR.

Contents

Introduction

Written over half a century ago, *Ethan Frome* has survived not only the changes in literary fashion but the occasional efforts, by critics of such imposing reputation as John Crowe Ransom and Lionel Trilling, to make us view it more severely and ask whether after all it is not merely a tour de force. "It is sometimes spoken of," says Mr. Trilling, ruefully, "as an American classic." Despite the reservations of some critics, the view that *Ethan Frome* is a classic has persisted, and attempts to chip away at the monument have left it strangely intact. Even Mrs. Wharton confessed to being "bored and exasperated" when told it was her best novel. It was not; it was simply her best known novel; and as such it had for a long time the effect of blocking our view of her more ambitious fiction. When it reached Broadway in dramatic form in 1936 the critics were obviously moved, but almost against their will, almost apologetically, as if skeptical of their response to a work that had earned its reputation too easily. It may be that in their general concern with the questions of technique and of Mrs. Wharton's credentials as a local colorist the critics of *Ethan Frome* have shifted their regard too exclusively from the center of the work to its periphery. Not the least curious trait in criticism of both the novel and the drama is its reluctance to admit that the muted love affair of Ethan Frome and Mattie Silver (written as we shall see out of Edith Wharton's deepest and most personal experience) is one of the most moving episodes in American fiction.

It is no slight on Mrs. Wharton's achievement to say that *Ethan Frome* lacks the moral energy and complexity and the richness of treatment of certain other American short novels, such as Melville's *Billy Budd,* James's *The Turn of the Screw,* or Faulkner's *The Bear.* That achievement was limited at the outset by her declared intentions. Her theme, she felt, had to be treated "as starkly and summarily as life had always presented itself to [her] protagonists." One may question this assumption, as some of her critics do, but only at the risk of raising questions that lie beyond the modest scope of Mrs. Wharton's aims.

When her most famous tale was published in 1911, Edith Wharton was an established writer, the author of five volumes of short stories, three novellas, three novels (among them the best-selling *The House of Mirth*), and several miscellaneous works, including a pioneer manual of interior decoration, a book of poems, and two books on Italy and one on France reflecting her love of travel, gardening, and architecture. Nothing in her earlier work had prepared her audience for *Ethan Frome.* Unlike so many novelists of her generation, who enlisted in the Progressive movement or joined the muckrakers in exposing the flaws in the economic and social structure, she had given no sign that she found the lives of the poor and desperate an attractive subject or one that fell within the scope of her observation. At the beginning of her career she had succumbed briefly to the vogue of the tenement tale (which also produced Stephen Crane's *Maggie*) and had written not only the forgotten "Mrs. Manstey's View," published in *Scribner's Magazine* in 1891, but the long tale "Bunner Sisters," which, though published five years after *Ethan Frome,* had been written as early as 1891 or 1892. But this was a vagary of the apprentice writer who had not yet discovered the material she could claim as peculiarly her own. Only

1

once, in *The House of Mirth* (1905), had she committed her full resources as a novelist to the subject she was best equipped to explore. It would have been impossible in 1911—indeed, it was only possible following the added testimony of *The Custom of the Country* (1913) and *The Age of Innocence* (1920)—to define her great subject as the decline of the old, benignly feudal, spiritually fibreless New York society in which she had grown up. There was a marked critical resistance early in the century to writers who evaded definition or who, once they were defined, struck off in new directions. Edith Wharton was thought of as a cosmopolitan, a rather formidable bluestocking, a "clever" writer (the adjective still clings to her reputation), and—vaguely and, as we know now, unfairly—as a disciple of her friend Henry James. Not surprisingly, *Ethan Frome* was received by many of its original audience with that mixture of skepticism and uneasiness which has persisted to this day. This grim fable of spiritual and emotional poverty, set in the wintry hills of New England, moved one reviewer to express the hope "that when Mrs. Wharton writes again she will bring her great talent to bear on normal people and situations."

A New Yorker by birth, Edith Wharton had temporarily adopted New England. For a part of each year, from 1901 to 1911, she and her husband occupied The Mount, in Lenox, Massachusetts, a house built largely to her design. (Even today, in a field behind The Mount, one can find, emerging from the thin soil, the "granite outcroppings" which Mrs. Wharton appropriated as her metaphor of the native character.) Whatever her grasp of local conditions so remote from her own, she had a direct intuition of the kind of tragedy possible in these surroundings. "This grim New England country," she once wrote to a friend, "for all its beauty, gives nothing to compensate for the complete mental starvation." Perhaps, as she implies in her memoirs, the world of

Starkfield, hitherto viewed through the "rose-coloured spectacles" of those nineteenth-century New England local colorists Sarah Orne Jewett and Mary Wilkins Freeman, demanded the scrutiny of a less partial observer—though this motive, the purely literary one, probably counts for least in the genesis of *Ethan Frome*. More simply compelling was the realist's impulse to treat with candor a way of life she had observed at close range. "For years," she recalled, "I had wanted to draw life as it really was in the derelict mountain villages of New England," and this motive is confirmed by a friend from the Lenox days who wrote:

One windy afternoon we were driving in the country near Lenox, and on the top of a hill on the left of the road stood a battered two-story house, unpainted, with a neglected door-yard tenanted by hens and chickens, and a few bedraggled children sitting on the stone steps before the open door. "It is about a place like that," said Mrs. Wharton, "that I mean to write a story. Only last week I went to the village meeting-house in Lenox and sat there for an hour alone, trying to think what such lives would be, and some day I shall write a story about it." [1]

Neither of these general motives—the impulse to correct the vision of her predecessors or the desire to record a way of life that solicited her imagination—had the force of the more personal motive. Now that the tragedy of Edith Wharton's marriage is more fully known and understood, we can see not only how it helped determine her choice of themes but how, at the deepest level, it helped her shape her treatment of those themes. In 1884, at the age of twenty-three, Edith Newbold Jones had married Edward Robbins ("Teddy") Wharton, a Philadelphian, twelve years her senior, an engaging person by all accounts, fond of gentlemanly sports, but totally uninterested in literature or ideas and clearly anything but the ideal partner for a young woman who as she became impatient with the role of society matron turned increasingly

[1] Percy Lubbock, *Portrait of Edith Wharton* (New York: D. Appleton-Century Company, 1947), pp. 22–23.

toward literature and the company of those who made it. For the first fifteen years of her marriage Edith Wharton held the leash on her literary ambitions, fulfilling the conventional demands of her role, playing hostess, gardening, travelling, and only occasionally and almost surreptitiously submitting a story to the magazines. It was the publication of her first collection of stories, *The Greater Inclination,* in 1899, that, as she says, "broke the chains which had held me so long in a kind of torpor." (There is even the story that she had taken up writing seriously, on the advice of the Philadelphia novelist and alienist S. Weir Mitchell, to avert a threatened nervous breakdown, and her letters to her editor at Charles Scribner's Sons in the mid-nineties confirm the occurrence of some sort of crisis in her health) .

In 1903 Edward Wharton suffered the first of a series of neurasthenic attacks—a second and more severe one followed five years later—which eventually reduced him to chronic and demanding invalidism. It may not be a coincidence, as Millicent Bell has pointed out, that his first breakdown came so closely on the heels of his wife's spiritual declaration of independence and her immediate success as a writer. The years that followed were difficult for them both. As Edward Wharton's condition deteriorated, as the attempts to confine him for treatment were thwarted, and as Edith Wharton's friends became more involved in her dilemma and more helpless to alleviate it (Henry James could only advise her to hold on and "go through the motions of life" until the evil should spend itself) , Mrs. Wharton came to depend more desperately on her vocation. These were the years when *Ethan Frome* was germinating in her mind and slowly, with revision after revision, being committed to manuscript. In 1913 the Whartons were divorced, but Edith Wharton had long since gone her separate way.

From beginning to end, Edith Wharton is preoccupied in her fiction with what I have called elsewhere "the trapped sensibility"—with the situation of the superior nature held in bondage by the inferior, seeking an avenue of escape, anxious to avoid sterile pain and what she called in "Bunner Sisters" the "inutility of self-sacrifice," anxious at the same time not to flout the conventions or to impose pain on others, and returning usually to the status quo or at best achieving some compromise, in deference to the claims of individual responsibility. This may be, as Lionel Trilling remarks of *Ethan Frome,* "the morality of inertia." But what should be kept in mind is that in story after story, novel after novel, Edith Wharton was trying to confront and perhaps even to rationalize her own situation; and to the degree that she was unsuccessful she has left readers like Mr. Trilling with the sense only of her faintheartedness, her incompetence, or at worst her dishonesty. If in *Ethan Frome* she temporized with the logic of her ending, as some of her critics insist, it is possible to understand why—from a biographical if not from an aesthetic point of view. To the extent that she was still a prisoner of her world and its values, and especially its attitude toward divorce or the evasion of any form of moral or legal commitment, and to the extent that she represented these values as operative in a world far different from her own, she did run the risk, as a novelist, of being dishonest. It is a question, at any rate, less easy to settle than to define.

There was still another element, however, in the novelist's personal situation. The Whartons' incompatibility and the slow dissolution of their marriage were only part of the actual dilemma which is projected in fictional terms in *Ethan Frome.* The year before her marriage Edith Wharton had met Walter Van Rensselaer Berry, member of an old New York family whose credentials were as unimpeachable as her own (they were in fact distant cousins) , a graduate of St. Marks and Harvard, and at the time of their meeting a law student in Washington, D.C. Half a century later Edith Wharton wrote guardedly of this most important encounter of her life: "We had seen a great deal of each other for a few weeks, and the encounter had given me a fleeting hint of what the communion of kindred intelligences might be." After her marriage they met again at infrequent intervals. During the writing of her first book, *The Decoration of Houses* (1897), Walter Berry became her literary mentor, and thereafter until his death, a decade before hers, he read her manuscripts (including *Ethan Frome*), criticized them, and helped her revise them. At what point the relationship became one of supreme importance in Edith Wharton's life is not clear; presumably it was in 1908, the year of Edward Wharton's second serious attack of neurasthenia. That she fell in love with Berry, still a bachelor and by now a figure in international social and legal circles; that he apparently fell short of matching her ardor and devotion; and that the consequence for Edith Wharton's emotional history, at a time when she desperately needed support, was a prolonged oscillation between moments of self-delusive joy and moments of frustration and despair—all this has been recorded. After her divorce she and Berry continued to be the closest of companions, but they never married. When he died in 1927 she wrote in her diary, "The light of all my life died today, and I with him." On her own death in 1937, she was at her request buried next to him in a Versailles cemetery.

The question of the relation of biographical "truth" to fictional "truth" is of course a precarious one. But there can be little doubt that the frustrating circumstances of Edith Wharton's personal dilemma were translated into fiction, not only in *Ethan Frome* but in many of her stories beginning most clearly with *The House of Mirth*. It is one of the elements that binds *Ethan Frome,* so apparently at first glance a departure from her usual subject, to the main body of her fiction. For Ethan, like his creator, is tied to an uncongenial partner, older than himself; like her, he experiences a vision of freedom through the appearance of someone he can love; and like her, finally, he is both willing to question the limits of responsibility and reluctant to achieve any happiness at a cost to others.

Given the variety of Edith Wharton's interests as a writer and the fact that the novels she had written before 1911 betray some uncertainty in handling the problems of the longer narrative structure, it is not surprising that she admitted in her memoirs, "It was not until I wrote 'Ethan Frome' that I suddenly felt the artisan's full control of his implements." This remark, made twenty years after the publication of the story, may, however, have been partly defensive. As the documents in this volume will indicate, it was precisely on the question of Mrs. Wharton's technique—her control of structure and point of view—that much of the critical debate over the years has been waged. It is apparent, nevertheless, from the fragmentary early version of the story (part of which is reproduced in the following pages) that the composition gave her unusual difficulties—or, to put it another way, that she took unusual pains to achieve the most lucid style, the appropriate idiom for her characters, the right relation between her framework narrative and the story proper, and to eliminate (how successfully is still a question) any patronizing overtones in her treatment of her New England types and their narrow mode of existence. How many revisions the story underwent, we may never know; the evidence, despite Mrs. Wharton's statement that it was "the book to the making of which I brought the greatest joy and the fullest ease," is that they were many. The fragment of the early version among her papers at Yale is a scissors-and-paste compilation from earlier versions, with new additions—the manuscript as a whole presenting a baffling problem to anyone who would try to distinguish the genetic stages of the work.

On its publication, first in three install-ments in *Scribner's Magazine* (August through October) and, on September 30, 1911, in book form, *Ethan Frome* was seri-ously reviewed on both sides of the At-lantic. To some reviewers its story was sor-did and unnecessarily painful, but they admitted its power and the art with which it was told. Its initial sale was slow (Edith Wharton complained that Scrib-ners was not publicizing it adequately). By 1922, however, it was so firmly estab-lished with a large public that Scribners reissued it in the Modern Student's Lib-rary with an introduction by the author. It has been in print continuously ever since.

PART ONE

THE STORY

Ethan Frome*

EDITH WHARTON (1862–1937) began *Ethan Frome* as an exercise in French, laid the tale aside for several years, then wrote the English version in Paris in the winter of 1910–1911. The story appeared in three installments in *Scribner's Magazine* in 1911 and was published in book form on September 30th of that year.

I had the story, bit by bit, from various people, and, as generally happens in such cases, each time it was a different story.

If you know Starkfield, Massachusetts, you know the post-office. If you know the post-office you must have seen Ethan Frome drive up to it, drop the reins on his hollow-backed bay and drag himself across the brick pavement to the white colonnade; and you must have asked who he was.

It was there that, several years ago, I saw him for the first time; and the sight pulled me up sharp. Even then he was the most striking figure in Starkfield, though he was but the ruin of a man. It was not so much his great height that marked him, for the "natives" were easily singled out by their lank longitude from the stockier foreign breed: it was the careless powerful look he had, in spite of a lameness checking each step like the jerk of a chain. There was something bleak and unapproachable in his face, and he was so stiffened and grizzled that I took him for an old man and was surprised to hear that he was not more than fifty-two. I had this from Harmon Gow, who had driven the stage from Bettsbridge to Starkfield in pre-trolley days, and knew the chronicle of all the families on his line.

"He's looked that way ever since he had his smash-up; and that's twenty-four years ago come next February," Harmon threw out between reminiscent pauses.

The "smash-up" it was—I gathered from the same informant—which, besides drawing the red gash across Ethan Frome's forehead, had so shortened and warped his right side that it cost him a visible effort to hobble from his buggy to the post-office window. He used to drive in from his farm every day at about midday, and as that was my own hour for fetching my mail I often passed him in the porch or stood beside him while we waited on the motions of the distributing hand behind the grating. I noticed that, though he came so punctually, he seldom received anything but a copy of the *Bettsbridge Eagle,* which he put without a glance into his sagging pocket. At intervals, however, the post-master would hand him an envelope addressed to Mrs. Zenobia—or Mrs. Zeena—Frome, and usually bearing conspicuously in the upper left-hand corner the address of some manufacturer of patent medicine and the name of his specific. These documents my neighbour would also pocket without a glance, as if too much used to them to wonder at their number and variety, and would then turn away with a silent nod to the post-master.

Every one in Starkfield knew him and gave him a greeting tempered to his own grave mien; but his taciturnity was re-

* Edith Wharton, "Ethan Frome," *Scribner's Magazine,* L (August, September, and October, 1911), 151–164, 317–334, 431–444.

spected and it was only on rare occasions that one of the older men of the place detained him for a word. When this happened he would listen quietly, his blue eyes on the speaker's face, and answer in so low a tone that his words never reached me; then he would climb stiffly into his buggy, gather up the reins in his left hand and drive slowly away in the direction of his farm.

"It was a pretty bad smash-up?" I questioned Harmon, looking after Frome's retreating figure, and thinking how gallantly his lean brown head, with its shock of light hair, must have sat on his shoulders before they were bent out of shape.

"Wust kind," my informant assented. "More'n enough to kill most men. But the Fromes are tough. Ethan'll likely touch a hundred."

"Good God!" I exclaimed. At the moment, Ethan Frome, after climbing to his seat, had leaned over to assure himself of the security of a wooden box—also with a druggist's label on it—which he had placed in the back of the buggy, and I saw his face as it probably looked when he thought himself alone. *"That* man touch a hundred? He looks as if he was dead and in hell now!"

Harmon drew a slab of tobacco from his pocket, cut off a wedge and pressed it into [151/152] the leather pouch of his cheek. "Guess he's been in Starkfield too many winters. Most of the smart ones get away."

"Why didn't *he?*"

Harmon considered. "Somebody had to stay and care for the folks. There warn't ever anybody but Ethan. Fust his father —then his mother—then his wife."

"And then the smash-up?"

Harmon chuckled sardonically. "That's so. He *had* to stay then."

"I see. And since then they've had to care for him?"

Harmon thoughtfully passed his tobacco to the other cheek. "Oh, as to that: I guess it's always Ethan done the caring."

Though Harmon Gow developed the tale as far as his mental and moral reach permitted there were perceptible gaps between his facts, and I had the sense that the deeper meaning of the story was in the gaps. But one phrase stuck in my memory and served as the nucleus about which I grouped my subsequent inferences: "Guess he's been in Starkfield too many winters."

Before my own time there was up I had learned to know what that meant. Yet I had come in the degenerate day of trolley, bicycle and rural delivery, when communication was easy between the scattered mountain villages, and the bigger towns in the valleys, such as Bettsbridge and Shadd's Falls, had libraries, theatres and Y.M.C.A. halls to which the youth of the hills could descend for recreation. But when winter shut down on Starkfield, and the village lay under a sheet of snow perpetually renewed from the pale skies, I began to see what life there—or rather its negation—must have been in Ethan Frome's young manhood.

I had been sent up by my employers on a job connected with the big power-house at Corbury Junction, and a long-drawn carpenters' strike had so delayed the work that I found myself anchored at Starkfield—the nearest habitable spot—for the best part of the winter. I chafed at first, and then, under the hypnotising effect of routine, gradually began to find a grim fascination in the life. During the early part of my stay I had been struck by the contrast between the vitality of the climate and the deadness of the community. Day by day, after the December snows were over, a blazing blue sky poured down torrents of light and air on the white landscape, which gave them back in an intenser glitter. One would have supposed that such an atmosphere must quicken the emotions as well as the blood; but it seemed to produce no change except that of retarding still more the sluggish pulse of Starkfield. When I had been there a little longer, and had seen this phase of crystal clearness followed by long stretches of sunless cold; when the storms of February had pitched their white tents about the devoted village and the wild cavalry of March winds had charged down to their support; I began to understand why Starkfield emerged from its six months' siege like a starved garrison capitulating without quarter. Twenty years earlier the means of resistance must have been far fewer, and the enemy in command of almost all the lines of access between the beleaguered villages; and, considering these things, I felt the sinister force of Harmon's phrase: "Most of the smart ones get away." But if that were the case, what had hindered the flight of a man like Ethan Frome?

During my stay at Starkfield I lodged with a middle-aged widow, colloquially known as Mrs. Ned Hale. Mrs. Hale's father had been the village lawyer of the previous generation, and "lawyer Varnum's house," where my landlady still lived with her mother, was the most considerable mansion in the village. It stood at one end of the main street, its classic portico and small-paned windows looking down a flagged path flanked with Norway spruces to the slim white steeple of the Congregational church. It was clear that the Varnum fortunes were at the ebb, but the two women did what they could to preserve a decent dignity; and Mrs. Hale, in particular, had a certain wan refinement not out of keeping with her pale old-fashioned house.

In the "best parlour," with its black horse-hair and mahogany weakly illuminated by a gurgling Carcel lamp, I listened every evening to another and more delicately shaded version of the Starkfield chronicle. It was not that Mrs. Ned Hale felt, or affected, any social superiority to the people about her; it was only that the accident of a finer sensibility and a little more education had put just enough distance between herself and her neighbours to enable her to judge them with detachment. She [**152/153**] was not unwilling to exercise this faculty, and I had great hopes of getting from her the missing facts of Ethan Frome's story, or rather the

key to his character which should coördinate the facts I knew. Her mind was a store-house of innocuous anecdote and any question about her acquaintance brought forth a flow of detail; but on the subject of Ethan Frome I found her unexpectedly reticent. There was no hint of disapproval in her reserve; I merely felt in her an insurmountable reluctance to speak of him or his affairs, a low "Yes, I knew them both . . . it was awful . . ." seeming to be the utmost concession that her distress could make to my curiosity.

So marked was the change in her manner, such depths of sad initiation did it imply, that, with some doubts as to my delicacy, I put the case to my village oracle, Harmon Gow; but got nothing for my pains but an uncomprehending grunt.

"Ruth Varnum was always as nervous as a rat; and she was the first one to see 'em after they was picked up. It happened right below lawyer Varnum's, down at the bend of the Corbury road, just round about the time that Ruth got engaged to Ned Hale. The young folks was all friends, and I guess she just can't bear to talk about it. She's had troubles enough of her own."

All the dwellers in Starkfield, as in more notable communities, had had troubles enough of their own to make them comparatively indifferent to those of their neighbours; and though all conceded that Ethan Frome's had been beyond the common measure, no one gave me an explanation of the look in his face which, as I persisted in thinking, neither poverty nor physical suffering could have put there. Nevertheless, I might have contented myself with the story pieced together from these hints had it not been for the provocation of Mrs. Hale's silence, and—a little later—for the accident of personal contact with the man.

On arriving at Starkfield I had arranged with Denis Eady, the rich Irish grocer, who was the proprietor of Starkfield's nearest approach to a livery stable, to send me over daily to Corbury Flats, where I had to pick up my train for the

Junction. But about the middle of the winter Eady's horses fell ill of a local epidemic. The illness spread to the other Starkfield stables and for a day or two I was put to it to find a means of transport. Then Harmon Gow suggested that Ethan Frome's bay was still on his legs and that his owner might be glad to drive me over.

I stared at the suggestion. "Ethan Frome? But I've never even spoken to him. Why on earth should he put himself out for me?"

Harmon's answer surprised me still more: "I don't know as he would; but I know he wouldn't be sorry to earn a dollar."

I had been told that Frome was poor, and that the saw-mill and the stony acres of his farm yielded scarcely enough to keep his household through the winter; but I had not supposed him to be in such want as Harmon's words implied, and I expressed my wonder.

"Well, matters ain't gone any too well with him," Harmon said. "When a man's been setting round like a hulk for twenty years or more, seeing things that want doing, it eats inter him, and he loses his grit. That Frome farm was always 'bout as bare's a milkpan when the cat's been round; and you know what one of them old-watermills is wuth nowadays. When Ethan could sweat over 'em both from sun-up to dark he kinder choked a living out of 'em; but his folks ate up most everything, even then, and I don't see how he makes out now. Fust his father got a kick, out haying, and went soft in the brain, and gave away money like Bible texts afore he died. Then his mother went queer and dragged along for years as weak as a baby; and his wife Zeena, she's always been the greatest hand at doctoring in the county. Sickness and trouble: that's what Ethan's had his plate full up with, ever since the very first helping."

The next morning, when I looked out, I saw the hollow-backed bay between the Varnum spruces, and Ethan Frome, throwing back his worn bear-skin, made room for me in the sleigh at his side. After that, for a week, he drove me over every morning to Corbury Flats, and on my return in the afternoon he met me again and carried me back through the icy night to Starkfield. The distance each way was barely three miles, but the old bay's pace was slow, and even with firm snow under the runners we were nearly an hour on the way. Ethan Frome drove in silence, the reins [**153/154**] loosely held in his left hand, his brown seamed profile under the helmet-like peak of the cap standing out against the banks of snow like the bronze relief of a hero. He never turned his face to mine, or answered, except in monosyllables, the questions I put, or such slight pleasantries as I ventured. He seemed a part of the mute melancholy landscape, an incarnation of its frozen woe, with all that was warm and sentient in him fast bound below the surface; but there was nothing unfriendly in his silence. I simply felt that he lived in a depth of moral isolation too remote for casual access, and I had the sense that his loneliness was not merely the result of his personal plight, tragic as I guessed that to be, but had in it the profound accumulated cold of many Starkfield winters.

Only once or twice was the distance between us bridged for a moment; and the glimpses thus gained confirmed my desire to know more. Once I happened to speak of an engineering job I had been on the previous winter in Florida, and of the contrast between the Starkfield landscape and that in which I had found myself the year before; and to my surprise Frome said suddenly: "Yes: I was down there once, and for a good while afterward I could call up the sight of it in winter. But now it's all snowed under."

He said no more, and I had to guess the rest from the inflection of his voice and his abrupt relapse into silence. Another day, on getting into my train at the Flats, I missed a volume of popular science—I think it was on some recent discoveries in bio-chemistry—which I had carried with me to read on the way. I thought no more about it till I got into the sleigh again that evening, and saw the book in Frome's hand.

"I found it after you were gone," he said.

I put the volume into my pocket and we dropped back into our usual silence; but as we began to crawl up the long hill from Corbury Flats to the Starkfield ridge I became aware in the dusk that he had turned his face to mine.

"There are things in that book that I didn't know the first word about," he said.

I wondered less at his words than at the queer note of resentment in his voice. He was evidently surprised and slightly aggrieved at his own ignorance.

"Does that sort of thing interest you?" I asked.

"It used to."

"There are one or two rather new things in the book: there have been some big strides lately in that particular line of research." I waited a moment for an answer that did not come; then I said: "If you'd like to look the book through I'd be glad to leave it with you."

He hesitated, and I had the impression that he felt himself about to yield to a stealing tide of inertia; then, "Thank you—I'll take it," he answered shortly.

I hoped that this incident might set up some more direct communication between us. Frome was so simple and straightforward that I was sure his curiosity about the book was based on a genuine interest in its subject. Such tastes and acquirements in a man of his condition made the contrast more poignant between his outer situation and his inner needs, and I hoped that the chance of giving expression to the latter might at least unseal his lips. But something in his past history, or in his present way of living, had apparently driven him too deeply into himself for any casual impulse to draw him back to his kind. At our next meeting he made no allusion to the book, and our intercourse seemed fated to re-main as negative and one-sided as if there had been no break in his reserve.

Frome had been driving me over to the Flats for about ten days when one morning I looked out of my window into densely falling snow. The height of the white waves massed against the garden-fence and along the wall of the church showed that the storm must have been going on all night, and that the drifts were likely to be heavy in the open. I thought it probable that my train would be delayed; but I had to be at the power-house for an hour or two that afternoon, and I decided, if Frome turned up, to drive over to the Flats and wait there till my train came in. I don't know why I put it in the conditional, however, for I never doubted that Frome would appear. He was not the kind of man to be turned from his business by any commotion of the elements; and at the appointed hour his sleigh glided up through the snow like a stage-apparition behind thickening veils of gauze.

I was getting to know him too well to express either wonder or gratitude at his keeping [**154/155**] his appointment; but I exclaimed in surprise as I saw him turn his horse in a direction opposite to that of the Corbury road.

"The railroad's blocked by a freight-train that got stuck in a drift below the Flats," he explained, as we jogged off through the stinging whiteness.

"But look here—where are you taking me, then?"

"Straight to the Junction, by the shortest way," he answered, pointing up School House Hill with his whip.

"To the Junction—in this storm? Why, it's a good ten miles!"

"The bay'll do it if you give him time. You said you had some business there this afternoon. I'll see you get there."

He said it so quietly that I could only answer: "You're doing me the biggest kind of a favour."

"That's all right," he rejoined.

Abreast of the school house the road forked, and we dipped down a lane to the left, between hemlock boughs bent inward to their trunks by the weight of the snow. I had often walked that way on Sundays, and knew that the solitary roof showing through bare branches near the bottom of the hill was that of Frome's saw-mill. It looked exanimate enough, with its idle wheel looming above the black stream dashed with yellow-white spume, and its cluster of sheds sagging under their white load. Frome did not even turn his head as we drove by, and still in silence we began to mount the next slope. About a mile farther, on a road I had never travelled, we came to an orchard of starved apple-trees writhing over a hill-side among outcroppings of slate that nuzzled up through the snow like animals pushing out their noses to breathe. Beyond the orchard lay a field or two, their boundaries lost under drifts; and above the fields, huddled against the white immensities of land and sky, one of those lonely New England farm-houses that make the landscape lonelier.

"That's my place," said Frome, with a sideway jerk of his lame elbow; and in the distress and oppression of the scene I did not know what to answer. The snow had ceased, and a flash of watery sunlight exposed the house on the slope above us in all its plaintive ugliness. The black wraith of a deciduous creeper flapped from the porch, and the thin wooden walls, under their worn coat of paint, seemed to shiver in the wind that had risen with the ceasing of the snow.

"The house was bigger in my father's time: I had to take down the 'L' a while back," Frome continued, checking with a twitch of the left rein the bay's evident intention of turning in through the broken-down gate.

I saw then that the unusually forlorn and stunted look of the house was partly due to the loss of what is known in New England as the "L": that long deep-roofed adjunct usually built at right angles to the main house, and connecting it, by way of store-rooms and tool-house, with the wood-shed and cow-barn.

Whether because of its symbolic sense, the image it presents of a life linked with the soil, and enclosing in itself the chief sources of warmth and nourishment, or whether merely because of the solace suggested by the thought that dwellers in that harsh climate can get to their morning's work without facing the weather, it is certain that the "L" rather than the house itself seems to be the centre, the actual hearth-stone, of the New England farm. Perhaps because of this connection of ideas, which had often occurred to me in my rambles about Starkfield, I heard a wistful note in Frome's words, and saw, in the diminished house, the image of his own shrunken body.

"We're kinder side-tracked here now," he added, "but there was considerable passing before the railroad was carried through to the Flats." He roused the lagging bay with another twitch; then, as if the mere sight of the house had let me too deeply into his confidence for any farther pretence of reserve, he went on slowly: "I've always set down the worst of mother's trouble to that. When she got the rheumatism so she couldn't move around she used to sit up there and watch the road by the hour; and one year, when they was six months mending the Bettsbridge pike after the floods, and Harmon Gow had to bring his stage round this way, she picked up so that she used to get down to the gate most days to see him. But after the trains begun running nobody ever come by here to speak of, and mother never could get it through her head what had happened, and it preyed on her right along till she died." [**155/156**]

As we turned into the Corbury road the snow began to fall again, cutting off our last glimpse of the lonely house; and Frome's silence fell with it, letting down between us the old veil of reticence. This time the wind did not cease with the return of the snow. Instead, it sprang up to a gale which now and then, from a tattered sky, flung pale sweeps of sunlight over a landscape chaotically tossed. But the bay was as good as Frome's word, and we pushed on to the Junction through the wild white scene.

In the afternoon the storm held off, and the clearness in the west seemed to my untrained eye the pledge of a fair evening. I finished my business as quickly as possible, and we set out for Starkfield with a fair chance of getting there for supper. But at sunset the storm-clouds gathered again, bringing with them an earlier night. The snow fell straight and steadily from a sky without wind, in a soft universal diffusion more confusing than the gusts and eddies of the morning: it seemed to be a part of the thickening darkness, to be the winter night itself descending on us layer by layer.

The small ray of Frome's lantern was soon lost in this smothering medium, in which even his sense of direction, and the bay's homing instinct, finally ceased to serve us. Two or three times some ghostly landmark sprang up to warn us that we were astray, and then was reabsorbed into the mist; and when we finally got back to our road the old horse began to show signs of exhaustion. I felt that I was to blame for having accepted Frome's offer, and after a short argument I persuaded him to let me get out of the sleigh and walk along through the snow at the bay's side. In this way we struggled on for another mile or two, and at last reached a point where Frome, peering into what seemed to me formless night, said: "That's my gate down yonder."

The last stretch had been the hardest part of the way. The bitter cold and the heavy going had nearly knocked the wind out of me, and I could feel the bay's side ticking like a clock under my hand.

"Look here, Frome," I began, "there's no earthly use in your going any farther—" but he interrupted me: "Nor you neither. There's been about enough of this for anybody."

I understood that he was offering me a night's shelter at the farm, and without answering I turned into the gate at his side, and followed him to the barn, where I helped him to unharness and bed down the tired horse. When this was done he unhooked the lantern from the sleigh, stepped out again into the night, and called to me over his shoulder: "This way."

Far off above us a square of light trembled through the screen of snow. Following in Frome's wake I floundered toward it, and in the darkness almost fell into one of the deep drifts against the front of the house. Frome scrambled up the slippery steps of the porch, digging a way through the snow with his heavily booted foot. Then he lifted his lantern, found the latch, and led the way into the house. I went after him into a low unlit passage, at the back of which a ladder-like staircase disappeared into obscurity. On our right a line of light marked the door of the room which had sent its ray across the night; and behind the door I heard a woman's voice droning querulously.

Frome stamped his feet on the threadbare oil-cloth to shake the snow from his boots, and set down his lantern on a kitchen chair which was the only piece of furniture in the hall. Then he opened the door.

"Come in," he said to me; and as he spoke the droning voice grew still. . .

It was that night that I found the clew to Ethan Frome, and began to put together this vision of his story. . . . . . .
. . . .
. . . .

I

The village lay under two feet of snow, with drifts at the windy corners. In a sky of iron the points of the Dipper hung like icicles and Orion flashed his cold fires. The moon had set, but the night was so transparent that the white housefronts between the elms looked gray against the snow, clumps of bushes made black stains on it, and the basement windows of the church sent shafts of yellow light far across the endless undulations.

Young Ethan Frome walked at a quick pace along the deserted street, past the bank and Michael Eady's new brick store and Lawyer Varnum's house with the two black Norway spruces at the gate. Opposite [156/157] the Varnum gate, where the road fell away toward the Corbury valley, the church reared its slim white steeple and narrow peristyle. As the young man walked toward it the upper windows drew a black arcade along the side wall of the building, but from the lower openings, on the side where the ground sloped steeply down to the Corbury road, the light shot its long bars, illuminating many fresh furrows in the track leading to the basement door, and showing, under an adjoining shed, a line of sleighs with heavily muffled horses.

The night was perfectly still, and the air so dry and pure that it gave little sensation of cold. The effect produced on Frome was rather of a complete absence of atmosphere, as though nothing less tenuous than ether intervened between the white earth under his feet and the metallic dome overhead. "It's like being in an exhausted receiver," he thought. Four or five years earlier he had taken a year's course at a technological college at Worcester, and dabbled in the laboratory with a friendly professor of physics; and the images supplied by that experience still cropped up, at unexpected moments, through the totally different associations of thought in which he had since been living. His father's death, and the misfortunes following it, had put a premature end to Ethan's studies; but though they had not gone far enough to be of much practical use they had fed his fancy and made him aware of huge cloudy meanings behind the daily face of things.

As he strode along through the snow the sense of such meanings glowed in his brain and mingled with the bodily flush produced by his sharp tramp. At the end of the village he paused before the darkened front of the church. He stood there a moment, breathing quickly, and looking up and down the street, in which not another figure moved. The pitch of the Corbury road, below Lawyer Varnum's spruces, was the favourite coasting-ground of Starkfield, and on clear evenings the church corner rang till late with the shouts of the coasters; but tonight not a sled darkened the whiteness of the long declivity. The silence of midnight lay on Starkfield, and all its waking life was gathered behind the church windows, from which strains of dance-music flowed with the broad bands of yellow light.

The young man walked around to the side of the building and went down the slope toward the basement door. To keep out of range of the revealing rays from within he made a circuit through the untrodden snow and gradually approached the farther angle of the basement wall. Thence, still hugging the shadow, he edged his way cautiously forward to the nearest window, holding back his straight spare body and craning his neck till he got a glimpse of the room.

Seen thus, from the pure and frosty darkness in which he stood, it seemed to be seething in a mist of heat. The metal reflectors of the gas-jets sent crude waves of light against the white-washed walls, and the iron flanks of the stove at the end of the hall looked as though they were heaving with volcanic fires. The floor was thronged with girls and young men. Down the side wall facing the window stood a row of kitchen chairs from which the older women had just risen. By this time the music had stopped, and the musicians—a fiddler, and the young lady who played the harmonium on Sundays —were hastily refreshing themselves at one corner of the supper-table which aligned its devastated pie-dishes and ice-cream saucers on the platform at the end of the room. The guests were preparing to leave, and the tide had already set toward the passage where coats and wraps were hung, when a young man with a sprightly foot and a shock of black hair shot into the middle of the floor and clapped his hands. The signal took instant effect. The musicians hurried to their instruments, the dancers—some already half-muffled for departure—fell into line down each side of the room, the older spectators slipped back to their chairs, and the lively young man, after diving about here and there in the throng, drew forth a girl who had already wound a cherry-coloured "fascinator" about her head, and, leading her up to the end of the room, whirled her down its length to the bounding tune of a Virginia reel.

Frome's heart was beating fast. He had been straining for a glimpse of the dark head under the cherry-coloured scarf and it vexed him that another eye should have been quicker than his. The leader of the reel, who looked as if he had Irish blood in his veins, danced well and his partner [157/158] caught his fire. As she passed down the line, her light figure swinging from hand to hand in circles of increasing swiftness, the scarf flew off her head and stood out behind her shoulders, and Frome, at each turn, caught sight of her laughing panting lips, the dark hair clouding about her forehead, and the dark eyes which seemed the only fixed points in a maze of flying lines.

The dancers were going faster and faster, and the musicians, to keep up with them, belaboured their instruments like jockeys lashing their mounts on the homestretch; yet it seemed to the young man at the window that the reel would never end. Now and then he turned his eyes from the girl's face to that of her partner, which, in the exhilaration of the dance, had taken on a look of almost impudent ownership. Denis Eady was the son of Michael Eady, the ambitious Irish grocer, whose suppleness and effrontery had given Starkfield its first notion of "smart" business methods, and whose new brick store testified to the success of the attempt. His son seemed likely to follow in his steps, and was meanwhile applying the same arts to the conquest of the Starkfield maidenhood. Hitherto Ethan Frome had been content to think him a mean

fellow; but now he positively invited a horse-whipping. It was strange that the girl did not seem aware of it: that she could lift her rapt face to her dancer's, and drop her hands into his without appearing to feel the offence of his look and touch.

Frome was in the habit of walking into Starkfield to fetch home his wife's cousin, Mattie Silver, on the rare evenings when some chance of amusement drew her to the village. It was his wife who had suggested, when the girl came to live with them, that such opportunities should be put in her way. Mattie Silver came from Stamford, and when she entered the Fromes' household to act as her cousin Zeena's aid it was thought best, as she came without pay, not to let her feel too sharp a contrast between the life she had left and the isolation of a Starkfield farm. But for this—as Frome sardonically reflected—it would hardly have occurred to Zeena to do anything for the girl's amusement.

When his wife first proposed that they should give Mattie an occasional evening out he had inwardly demurred at having to do the extra two miles to the village and back after his hard day on the farm; but not long afterward he had reached the point of wishing that Starkfield might give all its nights to revelry.

Mattie Silver had lived under his roof for a year, and from early morning till they met at supper he had frequent chances of seeing her; but no moments in her company were comparable to those when, her arm in his, and her light step flying to keep time with his long stride, they walked back through the night to the farm. He had taken to the girl from his first day, when he had driven over to the Flats to meet her, and she had smiled and waved to him from the train, and cried out "You must be Ethan!" as she jumped out with her bundles, while he reflected, looking over her slight person: "She don't look much on house-work, but she ain't a fretter, anyhow." But it was not only that the coming to his house of a bit of hopeful young life was like the lighting of a fire on a cold hearth. The girl was more than the bright serviceable creature he had thought her. She had an eye to see and an ear to hear: he could show her things and tell her things, and taste the bliss of feeling that all he imparted left long reverberations and echoes he could wake at will.

It was during their night walks back to the farm that he felt most intensely the sweetness of this communion. He had always been more sensitive than the people about him to the appeal of natural beauty. His unfinished studies had given form to this sensibility and even in his unhappiest moments field and sky spoke to him with a deep and powerful persuasion. But hitherto the emotion had remained in him as a silent ache, veiling with sadness the beauty that evoked it. He did not even know whether any one else in the world felt as he did, or whether he was the sole victim of this mournful privilege. Then he learned that one other spirit had trembled with the same touch of wonder: that at his side, living under his roof and eating his bread, was a creature to whom he could say: "That's Orion down yonder; the big fellow to the right is Aldebaran, and the bunch of little ones—like bees swarming—they're the Pleiades . . ." or whom he could hold entranced before a ledge of granite thrusting up through the fern while [158/159] he unrolled the huge panorama of the ice-age, and the long dim stretches of succeeding time. The fact that admiration for his learning mingled with Mattie's wonder at what he taught was not the least part of his pleasure. And there were other sensations, less definable but more exquisite, which drew them together with a shock of silent joy: the cold red of sunset behind winter hills, the flight of cloud-flocks over slopes of stubble, or the intensely blue shadows of hemlocks on sunlit snow. When she said to him once: "It looks just as if it was painted!" it seemed to Ethan that the art of definition could go no farther, and

that words had at last been found to utter his secret soul. . .

As he stood in the darkness outside the church these memories came back with the poignancy of vanished things. Watching Mattie whirl down the floor from hand to hand he wondered how he could ever have thought that his dull talk interested her. To him, who was never gay but in her presence, her gaiety seemed plain proof of indifference. The face she lifted to her dancers was the same which, when she saw him, always looked like a window that has caught the sunset. He even noticed two or three gestures which, in his fatuity, he had thought she kept for him: a way of throwing her head back when she was amused, as if to taste her laugh before she let it out, and a trick of sinking her lids slowly when anything charmed or moved her.

The sight made him unhappy, and his unhappiness awoke his latent fears. His wife had never shown any jealousy of Mattie, but of late she had grumbled increasingly over the house-work and found sardonic ways of attracting attention to the girl's inefficiency. Zeena had always been what Starkfield called "sickly," and Frome had to admit that, if she were as ailing as she believed, she needed the help of a stronger arm than the one which lay so lightly in his during the night walks to the farm. Mattie had no natural turn for house-keeping, and her training had done nothing to remedy this defect. She was quick to learn, but forgetful and dreamy, and not disposed to take the matter seriously. Ethan had an idea that if she were to marry a man she was fond of the dormant instinct would wake, and her pies and biscuits become the pride of the county; but domesticity in the abstract did not interest her. At first she was so awkward that he could not help laughing at her; but she laughed with him and that made them better friends. He did his best to supplement her unskilled efforts, getting up earlier than usual to light the kitchen fire, carrying in the wood overnight, and neglecting the mill for the farm that he might help her about the house during the day. He even crept down on Saturday nights to scrub the kitchen floor after the women had gone to bed; and Zeena, one day, had surprised him at the churn and had turned away with one of her queer looks.

Of late there had been other signs of her disfavour, as intangible but more disquieting. One cold winter morning, as he dressed in the dark, his candle flickering in the draught of the window, he had heard her voice from the bed behind him.

"The doctor don't want I should be left without anybody to do for me," she said in her flat whine.

He had supposed her to be asleep, and the sound of her voice had startled him, though she was given to abrupt explosions of speech after long intervals of secretive silence.

He turned and looked at her where she lay indistinctly outlined under the dark calico quilt, her high-boned face taking a grayish tinge from the whiteness of the pillow.

"Nobody to do for you?" he repeated.

"If you say you can't afford a hired girl when Mattie goes."

Frome turned away again, and taking up his razor stooped to catch the reflection of his stretched cheek in the blotched looking-glass above the wash-stand.

"Why on earth should Mattie go?"

"Well, when she gets married, I mean," his wife's drawl came from behind him.

"Oh, she'd never leave us as long as you needed her," he returned, scraping hard at his chin.

"I wouldn't ever have it said that I stood in the way of a poor girl like Mattie marrying a smart fellow like Denis Eady," Zeena answered in a tone of plaintive self-effacement.

Ethan, glaring at his face in the glass, threw his head back to draw the razor from ear to chin. His hand was steady, but the attitude was an excuse for not making an immediate reply. [**159/160**]

"And the doctor don't want I should be left without anybody," Zeena continued. "He wanted I should speak to you about a girl he's heard about, that might come—"

Ethan laid down the razor and straightened himself with a laugh.

"Denis Eady! If that's all, I guess there's no such hurry to look round for a girl."

"Well, I'd like to talk to you about it," said Zeena obstinately.

He was getting into his clothes in fumbling haste. "All right. But I haven't got the time now; I'm late as it is," he returned, holding his old silver turnip-watch to the candle.

Zeena, apparently accepting this as final, lay watching him in silence while he pulled his suspenders over his shoulders and jerked his arms into his coat; but as he went toward the door she said, suddenly and incisively: "I guess you're always late, now you shave every morning."

That thrust had frightened him more than any vague insinuations about Denis Eady. It was a fact that since Mattie Silver's coming he had taken to shaving every day; but his wife always seemed to be asleep when he left her side in the winter darkness, and he had stupidly assumed that she would not notice any change in his appearance. Once or twice in the past he had been faintly disquieted by Zenobia's way of letting things happen without seeming to remark them, and then, weeks afterward, in a casual phrase, revealing that she had all along taken her notes and drawn her inferences. Of late, however, there had been no room in his thoughts for such vague apprehensions. Zeena herself, from an oppressive reality, had faded into an insubstantial shade. All his life was lived in the sight and sound of Mattie Silver, and he could no longer conceive of its being otherwise. But now, as he stood outside the church, and saw Mattie spinning down the floor with Denis Eady, a throng of disregarded hints and menaces wove their cloud about his brain . . .

II

As the dancers poured out of the hall Frome drew back behind the projecting storm-door.

From this hidden corner he watched the segregation of the grotesquely muffled groups, in which a moving lantern ray now and then lit up a face flushed with food and dancing. The villagers, being afoot, were the first to climb the slope to the main street, while the country neighbours packed themselves into the sleighs under the shed.

"Ain't you riding, Mattie?" a woman's voice called back from the throng about the shed, and Ethan's heart gave a jump. From where he stood he could not see the persons coming out of the hall till they had advanced a few steps beyond the wooden sides of the storm-door; but through its cracks he heard a clear voice answer: "Mercy no! Not on such a night."

She was there, then, close to him, only a thin board between. In another moment she would step forth into the night, and his eyes, accustomed to the obscurity, would discern her as clearly as though she stood in daylight. A wave of shyness pulled him back into the dark angle of the wall, and he stood there in silence instead of making his presence known to her. It had been one of the wonders of their intercourse that from the first, she, the quicker, finer, more expressive, instead of crushing him by the contrast, had given him something of her own ease and freedom. But now he felt as heavy and loutish as in his student days, when he had tried to "jolly" the Worcester girls at a picnic.

He hung back, and she came out alone and paused within a few yards of him. She was almost the last to leave the hall, and she stood looking uncertainly about her as if wondering why he did not show himself. Then a man's figure approached, coming so close to her that under their formless wrappings they seemed merged in one dim outline.

"Gentleman friend gone back on you? Say, Matt, that's tough! No, I wouldn't be mean enough to tell the other girls. I ain't as low-down as that." (How Frome hated his cheap banter!) "But look at here, ain't it lucky I got the old man's cutter down there waiting for us?"

Frome heard the girl's voice, gaily incredulous: "What on earth's your father's cutter doin' down there?"

"Why, waiting for me to take a ride. I got the roan colt too. I kinder knew I'd want to take a ride to-night." Eady, in his triumph, tried to put a sentimental note into his bragging voice. [160/161]

The girl seemed to waver, and Frome saw her twirl the end of her scarf irresolutely about her fingers. Not for the world would he have made a sign to her, though it seemed to him that his life hung on her next gesture.

"Hold on a minute while I unhitch the colt," Denis called to her, springing toward the shed.

She stood perfectly still, looking after him, in an attitude of tranquil expectancy torturing to the hidden watcher. Frome noticed that she no longer turned her head from side to side, as though peering through the night for another figure. She let Denis Eady lead out the horse, climb into the cutter and fling back the bearskin to make room for her at his side; then, with a swift motion of flight, she darted up the slope toward the front of the church.

"Good-by! Hope you'll have a lovely ride!" she called back to him over her shoulder.

Denis laughed, and gave the horse a cut that brought him quickly abreast of the girl's retreating figure.

"Come along! Get in quick! It's as slippery as thunder on this turn," he cried, leaning over to reach out a hand to her.

She laughed back at him: "Good-night! I'm not getting in."

By this time they had passed beyond Frome's ear-shot and he could only follow the shadowy pantomime of their silhouettes as they continued to move along the crest of the slope above him. He saw Eady, after a moment, jump from the cutter and go toward the girl with the reins over one arm. The other he tried to slip through hers; but she eluded him quickly, and Frome's heart, which had swung out over a black void, trembled back to safety. A moment later he heard the jingle of departing sleigh bells and discerned a figure advancing alone toward the empty expanse of snow before the church.

In the black shade of the Varnum spruces he caught up with her and she turned with a quick "Oh!"

"Think I'd forgotten you, Matt?" he asked with boyish glee.

She answered seriously: "I thought maybe you couldn't come back for me."

"Couldn't? What on earth could stop me?"

"I knew Zeena wasn't feeling any too good to-day."

"Oh, she's in bed long ago." He stopped, a question struggling in him. "Then you meant to walk home all alone?"

"Oh, I ain't afraid!" she laughed.

They stood together in the gloom of the spruces, an empty world glimmering about them wide and grey under the stars. He brought his question out.

"If you thought I hadn't come, why didn't you ride back with Denis Eady?"

"Why, where *were* you? How did you know? I never saw you!"

Her wonder and his laughter ran together like spring rills in a thaw. Ethan had the sense of having done something arch and ingenious. To prolong the effect he groped for a dazzling phrase, and brought out, in a growl of rapture: "Come along."

He slipped an arm through hers, as Eady had done, and fancied it was faintly pressed against her side; but neither of them moved. It was so dark under the spruces that he could barely see the shape of her head beside his shoulder. He longed to stoop his cheek and rub it against her scarf. He would have liked to stand there with her all night in the blackness. She moved forward a step or two and then paused again above the dip of the Corbury road. Its icy slope, scored by innumerable runners, looked like a mirror scratched by travellers at an inn.

"There was a whole lot of them coasting before the moon set," she said.

"Would you like to come in and coast with them some night?" he asked.

"Oh, *would* you, Ethan? It would be lovely!"

"We'll come to-morrow if there's a moon."

She lingered, pressing closer to his side. "Ned Hale and Ruth Varnum came just as *near* running into the big elm at the bottom. We were all sure they were killed." Her shiver ran down his arm. "Wouldn't it have been too awful? They're so happy!"

"Oh, Ned ain't much at steering. I guess I can take you down all right!" he said disdainfully.

He was aware that he was "talking big," like Denis Eady; but his reaction of joy had unsteadied him, and the inflection with which she had said of the engaged couple "They're so happy!" made the [161/162] words sound as if she had been thinking of herself and him.

"The elm *is* dangerous, though. It ought to be cut down," she insisted.

"Would you be afraid of it, with me?"

"I told you I ain't the kind to be afraid," she tossed back, almost indifferently; and suddenly she began to walk on with a rapid step.

These alternations of mood were the despair and joy of Ethan Frome. The motions of her mind were as incalculable as the flit of a bird in the branches. The fact that he had no right to show his feelings, and thus provoke the expression of hers, made him attach a fantastic importance to every change in her look and tone. Now he thought she understood him, and feared; now he was sure she did not, and despaired. To-night the pressure of accumulated misgivings sent the scale drooping toward despair, and her indifference was the more chilling after the flush of joy into which she had plunged him by dismissing Denis Eady. He mounted School House Hill at her side and walked on in silence till they reached the lane leading to the saw-mill; then the need of some definite assurance grew too strong for him.

"You'd have found me right off if you hadn't gone back to have that last reel with Denis," he brought out awkwardly. He could not pronounce the name without a stiffening of the muscles of his throat.

"Why, Ethan, how could I tell you were there?"

"I suppose what folks say is true," he jerked out at her, instead of answering.

She stopped short, and he felt, in the darkness, that her face was lifted quickly to his. "Why, what do folks say?"

"It's natural enough you should be leaving us," he floundered on, following his thought.

"Is that what they say?" she mocked back at him; then, with a sudden drop of her sweet treble: "You mean that Zeena —ain't suited with me any more?" she faltered.

Their arms had slipped apart and they stood motionless, each seeking to distinguish the other's face.

"I know I ain't anything like as smart as I ought to be," she went on, while he vainly struggled for expression. "There's lots of things a hired girl could do that come awkward to me still—and I haven't got much strength in my arms. But if she'd only tell me I'd try. You know she hardly ever says anything, and sometimes I can see she ain't suited, and yet I don't know why." She turned on him with a sudden flash of indignation. "You'd ought to tell me, Ethan Frome—you'd ought to! Unless *you* want me to go too——"

Unless he wanted her to go too! The cry was balm to his raw wound. The iron heavens seemed to melt and rain down sweetness. Again he struggled for the all-expressive word, and again, his arm in hers found only a deep "Come along."

They walked on in silence through the blackness of the hemlock-shaded lane, where Ethan's saw-mill gloomed through the night, and out again into the relative clearness of the fields. On the farther side of the hemlock belt the open country rolled away before them grey and lonely under the stars. Sometimes their way led them under the shade of an overhanging bank or through the thin obscurity of a clump of leafless trees. Here and there a farm-house stood far back among the fields, mute and cold as a grave-stone. The night was so still that they heard the frozen snow crackle under their feet. Now and then they were startled by the crash of a loaded branch falling suddenly far off in the woods; and once a fox barked, and Mattie shrank closer to Ethan, and quickened her steps.

At length they sighted the group of larches at Ethan's gate, and as they drew near it the sense that the walk was over brought back his words.

"Then you don't want to leave us, Matt?"

He had to stoop his head to catch her stifled whisper: "Where'd I go, if I did?"

The answer sent a pang through him but the tone suffused him with joy. He forgot what else he had meant to say and pressed her against him so closely that he seemed to feel her warmth.

"You ain't crying are you, Matt?"

"No, of course I'm not," she quavered.

They turned in at the gate and passed under the knoll where, enclosed in a low fence, the Frome grave-stones slanted at crazy angles through the snow. Ethan looked at them curiously. For years that quiet company had mocked his restlessness, his desire for change and freedom. [162/163] "We never got away—how should you?" seemed to be written on every headstone; and whenever he went in or out of his gate he thought with a shiver: "I shall just go on living here till I join them." But now all desire for change had vanished, and the sight of the little enclosure gave him a warm sense of continuance and stability.

"I guess we'll never let you go, Matt,"

he whispered, thinking, as they brushed by the graves: "We'll always go on living here together, and some day she'll lie there beside me."

He let the vision possess him as they climbed the hill to the house. He was never so happy with her as when he abandoned himself to these dreams. Half-way up the slope Mattie stumbled against some unseen obstruction and clutched his sleeve to steady herself. The wave of warmth that went through him was like the prolongation of his vision. For the first time he stole his arm about her, and she did not resist. They walked on as if they were floating on a summer stream.

Zeena always went to bed as soon as she had had her supper, and the shutterless windows of the house were dark. A dead cucumber-vine dangled from the porch like the crape streamer tied to the door for a death, and the thought flashed through Ethan's brain: "If it was there for Zeena—" Then he had a distinct sight of his wife lying in their bedroom asleep, her mouth slightly open, her false teeth in a tumbler by the bed . . .

They walked around to the back of the house, between the rigid gooseberry bushes. It was Zeena's habit, when they came back late from the village, to leave the key of the kitchen door under the mat. Ethan stood before the door, his head heavy with dreams, his arm still about Mattie. "Matt—" he began, not knowing what he meant to say.

She slipped out of his hold without speaking, and he stooped down and felt for the key.

"It's not there!" he said, straightening himself with a start.

They strained their eyes at each other through the icy darkness. Such a thing had never happened before.

"Maybe she's forgotten it," Mattie said in a tremulous whisper; but both of them knew that it was not like Zeena to forget.

"Maybe it's fallen off into the snow," Mattie continued, after a pause during which they had stood intently listening.

"It must have been pushed off, then," he rejoined in the same tone. Another wild thought tore through him. What if tramps had been there, and what if . . .

Again he strained his ears, fancying he heard a sound in the house, then he felt in his pocket for a match, and kneeling down, passed its light slowly over the rough edges of snow about the doorstep.

He was still kneeling when his eyes, on a level with the lower part of the door, caught a faint ray beneath it. Who could be stirring in that silent house? He heard a step on the stairs, and again for an instant the thought of tramps tore through him. Then the door opened and he saw his wife.

Against the dark background of the kitchen she stood up tall and angular, one hand drawing a quilted counterpane to her flat breast, while the other held a lamp. The light, on a level with her chin, drew out of the darkness her puckered throat and the projecting wrist of the hand that clutched the quilt, and deepened fantastically the hollows and prominences of her high-boned face under its ring of crimping-pins. To Ethan, still in the rosy haze of his hour with Mattie, the sight came with the intense precision of the last dream before waking. He felt as if he had never before known what his wife looked like.

She drew aside without speaking, and Mattie and Ethan passed into the kitchen, which had the deadly chill of a vault after the dry cold of the night.

"Guess you forgot about us, Zeena," Ethan joked, stamping the snow from his boots.

"No. I just felt so mean I couldn't sleep."

Mattie came forward, unwinding her wraps, the colour of the cherry scarf in her fresh lips and cheeks. "I'm so sorry, Zeena! Isn't there anything I can do?"

"No, there's nothing." Zeena turned away from her. "You might 'a' shook off that snow outside," she said to her husband.

She walked out of the kitchen ahead of them and, pausing in the hall, raised the lamp at arm's-length as if to light them up the stairs.

Ethan paused also, affecting to fumble for the peg on which he hung his coat and [**163/164**] cap. The doors of the two bedrooms faced each other across the narrow upper landing, and to-night it was peculiarly repugnant to him that Mattie should see him follow Zeena.

"I guess I won't come up yet awhile," he said, turning as if to go back to the kitchen.

Zeena stopped short and looked at him. "For the land's sake—what you going to do down here?"

"I've got the mill accounts to go over."

She continued to stare at him, the flame of the unshaded lamp bringing out with microscopic cruelty the fretful lines of her face.

"At this time o' night? You'll ketch your death. The fire's out long ago."

Without answering he moved away toward the kitchen. As he did so his glance crossed Mattie's and he fancied that a fugitive warning gleamed through her lashes. The next moment they sank to her flushed cheeks and she began to mount the stairs ahead of Zeena.

"That's so. It *is* powerful cold down here," Ethan assented; and with lowered head he went up in his wife's wake, and followed her across the threshold of their room. [**164/317**]

III

There was some hauling to be done at the lower end of the wood-lot, and Ethan was out early the next day.

The winter morning was as clear as crystal. The sunrise burned red in a pure sky, the shadows on the rim of the wood-lot were darkly blue, and beyond the white fields patches of far-off forest hung like smoke.

It was in the early morning stillness, when his muscles were swinging to their familiar task and his lungs expanding with long draughts of mountain air, that Ethan did his clearest thinking. He and Zeena had not exchanged a word after the door of their room had closed on

them. She had measured out some drops from a medicine-bottle on a chair by the bed and, after swallowing them, and wrapping her head in a piece of yellow flannel, had lain down with her face turned away. Ethan undressed hurriedly and blew out the light so that he should not see her when he took his place at her side. As he lay there he could hear Mattie moving about in her room, and her candle, sending its small ray across the landing, drew a scarcely perceptible line of light under his door. He kept his eyes fixed on the light till it vanished. Then the room grew perfectly black, and not a sound was to be heard but Zeena's asthmatic breathing. Ethan felt confusedly that there were many things he ought to think about, but through his tingling veins and tired brain only one sensation throbbed: the warmth of Mattie's shoulder against his. Why had he not kissed her when he held her there? A few hours earlier he would not have asked himself the question. Even a few minutes earlier, when they had stood alone outside the house, he would not have dared to think of kissing her. But since he had seen her lips in the lamplight he felt that they were his.

Now, in the bright morning air, her face was still before him. It was part of the sun's red and of the pure glitter on the snow. How the girl had changed since she had come to Starkfield! He remembered what a colourless slip of a thing she had looked the day he had met her at the station. And all the first winter, how she had shivered with cold when the northerly gales shook the thin clapboards and the snow beat like hail against the loose-hung windows!

He had been afraid that she would hate the hard life, the cold and loneliness; but not a sign of discontent escaped her. Zeena took the view that Mattie was bound to make the best of Starkfield since she hadn't any other place to go to; but this did not strike Ethan as conclusive. Zeena, at any rate, did not apply the principle in her own case.

He felt all the more sorry for the girl because misfortune had, in a sense, indentured her to them. Mattie Silver was the daughter of a cousin of Zenobia Frome's, who had inflamed his clan with mingled sentiments of envy and admiration by descending from the hills to Connecticut, where he had married a Stamford girl and succeeded to her father's thriving "drug" business. Unhappily Orin Silver, a man of far-reaching aims, had died too soon to prove that the end justifies the means. His accounts revealed merely what the means had been; and these were such that it was fortunate for his wife and daughter that his books were examined only after his impressive funeral. His wife died of the disclosure, and Mattie, at twenty, was left alone to make her way on the fifty dollars obtained from the sale of her piano. For this purpose her equipment, though varied, was inadequate. She could trim a hat, make molasses candy, recite "Curfew shall not ring to-night," and play "The Lost Chord" and a potpourri from "Carmen." When she tried to extend the field of her activities in the direction of stenography and bookkeeping her health broke down, and six months on her feet behind the counter of a department store did not tend to restore it. Her nearest relations had been induced to place their savings in her father's hands, [**317/318**] and though, after his death, they ungrudgingly acquitted themselves of the Christian duty of returning good for evil by giving his daughter all the advice at their disposal, they could hardly be expected to supplement it by material aid. But when Zenobia's doctor advised her to look about for some one to help her with the house-work the clan instantly saw the chance of exacting a compensation from Mattie. Zenobia was doubtful of the girl's efficiency, but tempted by the freedom to find fault without much risk of losing her; and so Mattie came to Starkfield.

Zenobia's fault-finding was of the silent kind, but not the less discouraging for that. During the first months Ethan alternately burned with the desire to see Mattie defy her and trembled with fear of the result. Then the situation grew less strained. The pure air, and the long summer hours in the open, gave back life and elasticity to Mattie, and Zeena, with more leisure to devote to her complex ailments, grew less watchful of the girl's omissions; so that Ethan, struggling on under the burden of his barren farm and failing saw-mill, could at least imagine that peace reigned in his house.

There was really, as yet, no evidence to the contrary; but since the previous night a vague dread had hung on his sky-line. It was formed of Zeena's obstinate silence, of Mattie's sudden look of warning, of the memory of just such fleeting imperceptible signs as those which told him, on certain stainless mornings, that before night there would be rain.

His dread was so strong that, man-like, he sought to postpone certainty. The hauling was not over till mid-day, and as the lumber was to be delivered to Andrew Hale, the Starkfield builder, it was really easier for Ethan to send Jotham Powell, the hired man, back to the farm on foot, and drive the load down to the village himself. He had scrambled up on the logs, and was sitting astride of them, close over his shaggy grays, when, coming between him and their steaming necks, he had a vision of the warning look that Mattie had given him the night before.

"If there's going to be any trouble I want to be there," was his vague reflection, as he threw to Jotham the unexpected order to unhitch the team and lead them back to the barn.

It was a slow trudge home through the heavy fields, and when the two men entered the kitchen Mattie was lifting the coffee from the stove and Zeena was already at the table. Her husband stopped short at sight of her. Instead of her usual calico wrapper and knitted shawl she wore her best dress of brown merino, and from her thin strands of hair, which still held the tight undulations of the crimping-pins, rose a hard perpendicular bon-

net, as to which Ethan's clearest notion
was that he had had to pay five dollars
for it at the Bettsbridge Emporium. On
the floor beside her stood his old valise
and a bandbox wrapped in newspapers.

"Why, where are you going, Zeena?"
he exclaimed.

"I've got my shooting pains so bad that
I'm going over to Bettsbridge to spend
the night with Aunt Martha Pierce and
see that new doctor," she answered in a
matter-of-fact tone, as if she had said she
was going into the store-room to take a
look at the preserves, or up to the attic to
go over the blankets.

In spite of Zeena's sedentary habits
such abrupt decisions were not without
precedent in her history. Twice or thrice
before she had suddenly packed Ethan's
valise and started off for Bettsbridge, or
even Springfield, to seek the advice of
some new doctor, and her husband had
grown to dread these expeditions because
of their cost. Zeena always came back
laden with expensive remedies, and her
last visit to Springfield had been com-
memorated by her paying twenty dollars
for an electric battery of which she had
never been able to learn the use. But for
the moment his sense of relief was so
great that it precluded all other feelings.
He had now no doubt that Zeena had
spoken the truth in saying, the night before, that she had sat up because she felt
"too mean" to sleep: her abrupt resolve
to seek medical advice showed that, as
usual, she was wholly absorbed in her
health.

As if expecting a protest, she continued
plaintively: "If you're too busy with the
hauling I presume you can let Jotham
Powell drive me over with the sorrel in
time to ketch the train at the Flats."

Her husband hardly heard her. He was
lost in a rapid calculation. During the
winter months there was no stage between [318/319] Starkfield and Bettsbridge, and the trains which stopped at
Corbury Flats were slow and infrequent.
Zeena could not be back at the farm before the following evening . . .

"If I'd supposed you'd 'a' made any
objection to Jotham Powell's driving me
over—" she began again, as if his silence
had implied refusal. On the brink of departure she was always seized with a flux
of words. "All I know is," she continued,
"I can't go on the way I am much longer.
The pains are clear down to my ankles
now, or I'd 'a' walked in to Starkfield on
my own feet, sooner'n put you out, and
asked Michael Eady to let me ride over
on his wagon to the Flats, when he sends
to meet the train that brings his groce-
ries. I'd 'a' had two hours to wait in the
station, but I'd sooner 'a' done it, even
with this cold, than to have you say——"

"Of course Jotham'll drive you over,"
Ethan roused himself to answer. He became suddenly conscious that he was looking at Mattie while Zeena talked to him,
and with an effort he turned his eyes to
his wife. She sat opposite the window,
and the pale light reflected from the
banks of snow made her face look more
than usually drawn and bloodless, sharpened the three parallel creases between
ear and cheek, and drew querulous lines
from her thin nose to the corners of her
mouth. Though she was but six years her
husband's senior, and he was only twenty-
eight, she was already an old woman.

Ethan tried to say something befitting
the occasion, but there was only one
thought in his mind: the fact that, for
the first time since Mattie had come to
live with them, Zeena was to be away for
a night. He wondered if the girl were
thinking of it too . . . He knew that
Zeena must be wondering why he did not
offer to drive her over to the Flats and let
Jotham Powell take the lumber in to
Starkfield, and at first he could not think
of a pretext for not doing so; then he
said: "I'd take you over myself, only I've
got to collect the cash for the lumber."

As soon as the words were spoken he
regretted them, not only because they
were untrue—there being no prospect of
his receiving cash payment from Hale—
but also because he knew from experience the imprudence of letting Zeena

think he was in funds on the eve of one of her therapeutic excursions. At the moment, however, his one desire was to avoid the long drive with her behind the ancient sorrel who never went out of a walk.

Zeena made no reply: she did not seem to hear what he had said. She had already pushed her plate aside, and was measuring out a draught from a large bottle at her elbow.

"It ain't done me a speck of good, but I guess I might as well use it up," she remarked; adding, as she pushed the empty bottle toward Mattie: "If you can get the taste out it'll do for the pickles."

IV

As soon as his wife had driven off Ethan took his coat and cap from the peg. Mattie was washing up the dishes, humming one of the dance tunes of the night before. He said "So long, Matt," and she answered gaily "So long, Ethan"; and that was all.

It was warm and bright in the kitchen. The sun slanted through the south window on the girl's moving figure, on the cat dozing in a chair, and on the geraniums brought in from the door-way, where Ethan had planted them in the summer to "make a garden" for Mattie. He would have liked to linger on, watching her tidy up and then settle down to her sewing; but he wanted still more to get the hauling done and be back at the farm before night.

All the way down to the village he continued to think of his return to Mattie. The kitchen was a poor place, not "spruce" and shining as his mother had kept it in his boyhood; but it was surprising what a homelike look the mere fact of Zeena's absence gave it. And he pictured how it would look that evening, when he and Mattie were there after supper. For the first time they would be alone together indoors, and they would sit there, one on each side of the stove, like a married couple, he in his stocking

feet and smoking his pipe, she laughing and talking in that funny way she had, which was always as new to him as if he had never heard her before.

The sweetness of the picture, and the relief of knowing that his fears of "trouble" with Zeena were unfounded, sent up his spirits with a rush, and he, who was usually [**319/320**] so silent, whistled and sang aloud as he drove through the snowy fields. There was in him a slumbering spark of sociability which the long Starkfield winters had not yet extinguished. By nature grave and inarticulate, he admired recklessness and gaiety in others and was warmed to the marrow by friendly human intercourse. At Worcester, though he had the name of keeping to himself and not being much of a hand at a good time, he had secretly gloried in being clapped on the back and hailed as "Old Ethe" or "Old Stiff"; and the cessation of such familiarities had increased the chill of his return to Starkfield.

There the silence had deepened about him year by year. Left alone, after his father's accident, to carry the burden of farm and mill, he had had no time for convivial loiterings in the village; and when his mother fell ill the loneliness of the house grew deeper than that of the fields. His mother had been a talker in her day, but after her "trouble" the sound of her voice was seldom heard, though she had not lost the power of speech. Sometimes, in the long winter evenings when, in desperation, her son asked her why she didn't "say something," she would lift a finger and answer: "Because I'm listening"; and on stormy nights, when the wind was about the house, she would complain, if he spoke to her: "They're talking so out there that I can't hear you."

It was only when she drew toward her last illness, and his cousin Zenobia Pierce came over from the next valley to help him nurse her, that human speech was heard again in the house. After the mortal silence of his long imprisonment

Zeena's volubility was music in his ears. He felt that he might have "gone like his mother" if the sound of a new voice had not come to steady him. Zeena seemed to understand his case at a glance. She laughed at him for not knowing the simplest sick-bed duties and told him to "go right along out" and leave her to see to things. The mere fact of obeying her orders, of feeling free to go about his business again and talk with other men, restored his shaken balance and magnified his sense of what he owed her. Her efficiency shamed and dazzled him. She seemed to possess by instinct all the household wisdom that his long apprenticeship had not taught him. When the end came it was she who had to tell him to hitch up and go for the undertaker; and she thought it "funny" that he had not settled beforehand who was to have his mother's clothes and the sewing-machine. After the funeral, when he saw her preparing to go away, he was seized with an unreasoning dread of being left alone on the farm; and before he knew what he was doing he had asked her to stay there with him. He had often thought since that it would not have happened if his mother had died in spring instead of winter . . .

When they married it was agreed that, as soon as he could straighten out the difficulties resulting from his mother's long illness, they would sell the farm and saw-mill and try their luck in a large town. Ethan's love of nature did not take the form of a taste for agriculture. He had always wanted to be an engineer, and to live in towns, where there were lectures and big libraries and "fellows doing things." A slight engineering job in Florida, put in his way during his period of study at Worcester, increased his faith in his ability as well as his eagerness to see the world; and he felt sure that, with a "smart" wife like Zeena, it would not be long before he had made himself a place in it.

Zeena's native village was slightly larger and nearer to the railway than Starkfield, and she had let her husband see from the first that life on an isolated farm was not what she had expected when she married. But purchasers were slow in coming and while he waited for them Ethan learned the impossibility of transplanting her. She chose to look down on Starkfield, but she could not have lived in a place which looked down on her. Even Bettsbridge or Shadd's Falls would not have been sufficiently aware of her, and in the greater cities which attracted Ethan she would have suffered a complete loss of identity. And within a year of their marriage she developed the "sickliness" which had since made her notable even in a community rich in pathological instances. When she came to take care of his mother she had seemed to Ethan like the very genius of health, but he soon saw that her skill as a nurse had been acquired by the absorbed observation of her own symptoms.

Then she too fell silent. Perhaps it was the inevitable effect of life on the farm, or [**320/321**] perhaps, as she sometimes said, it was because Ethan "never listened." The charge was not wholly unfounded. When she spoke it was only to complain, and to complain of things not in his power to remedy; and to check a tendency to impatient retort he had first formed the habit of not answering her, and finally of thinking of other things while she talked. Of late, however, since he had had reasons for observing her more closely, her silence had begun to trouble him. He recalled his mother's growing taciturnity, and wondered if Zeena were also turning "queer." Women did, he knew. Zeena, who had at her fingers' ends the pathological chart of the whole region, had cited many cases of the kind while she was nursing his mother; and he himself knew of certain lonely farm-houses in the neighbourhood where stricken creatures pined, and of others where sudden tragedy had come of their presence. At times, looking at Zeena's shut face, he felt the chill of such forebodings. At other times her silence seemed deliberately assumed to conceal far-reaching intentions, mysterious conclusions drawn from suspicions and resentments impossible to guess. That supposition was even more disturbing than the other; and it was the one which had come to him the night before, when he had seen her standing in the kitchen door.

Now her departure for Bettsbridge had once more eased his mind, and all his thoughts were on the prospect of his evening with Mattie. Only one thing weighed on him, and that was his having told Zeena that he was to receive cash for the lumber. He foresaw so clearly the consequences of this imprudence that with considerable reluctance he decided to ask Andrew Hale for a small advance on his load.

When Ethan drove into Hale's yard the builder was just getting out of his sleigh.

"Hello, Ethe!" he said. "This comes handy."

Andrew Hale was a ruddy man with a big gray moustache and a stubbly double-chin unconstrained by a collar; but his scrupulously clean shirt was always fastened by a small diamond stud. This display of opulence was misleading, for though he did a fairly good business it was known that his easy-going habits and the demands of his large family frequently kept him what Starkfield called "behind." He was an old friend of Ethan's family, and his house one of the few to which Zeena occasionally went, drawn there by the fact that Mrs. Hale, in her youth, had done more "doctoring" than any other woman in Starkfield, and was still a recognized authority on symptoms and treatment.

Hale went up to the grays and patted their sweating flanks.

"Well, sir," he said, "you keep them two as if they was pets."

Ethan set about unloading the logs and when he had finished his job he pushed open the glazed door of the shed which the builder used as his office. Hale sat with his feet up on the stove, his back propped against a battered desk strewn with papers: the place, like the man, was warm, genial, and untidy.

"Sit right down and thaw out," he greeted Ethan.

The latter did not know how to begin, but at length he managed to bring out his request for an advance of fifty dollars. Under the sting of Hale's surprise, the blood mounted to Ethan's thin skin. It was the builder's custom to pay at the end of three months, and there was no precedent between the two men for a cash settlement. Ethan felt that if he had pleaded an urgent need Hale might have made shift to pay him; but pride, and an instinctive prudence, kept him from resorting to this argument. After his father's death it had taken time to get his head above water, and he did not want Andrew Hale, or any one else in Starkfield, to think he was going under again. Besides, he hated lying: if he wanted the money he wanted it, and it was nobody's business to ask why. He therefore put his request with the awkwardness of a proud man who will not admit to himself that he is stooping; and he was not much surprised at Hale's refusal.

The builder refused genially, as he did everything else: he treated the matter as something in the nature of a practical joke, and wanted to know if Ethan meditated buying a grand piano or adding a "cupolo" to his house: offering, in the latter case, to give his services free of cost.

Ethan's arts were soon exhausted, and after an embarrassed pause he wished Hale good day and opened the door of the office. As he passed out the builder suddenly [**321/322**] called after him: "See here—you ain't in a tight place, are you?"

"Not a bit," Ethan's pride retorted, before his reason had time to intervene.

"Well, that's good! Because I *am,* a shade. Fact is, I was going to ask you to give me a little extra time on that payment. Business is pretty slack, to begin with, and then I'm fixing up a little house for Ned and Ruth when they're married. I'm glad to do it for 'em, but it costs." His look appealed to Ethan for sympathy. "The young people like things nice. You know how it is yourself: it's not so long ago since you fixed up your own place for Zeena."

Ethan left the grays in Hale's stable and went about some other business in the village. As he walked away the builder's last phrase lingered in his ears, and he reflected grimly that his seven years with Zeena seemed to Starkfield "not so long."

The afternoon was drawing to an end, and here and there a lighted pane spangled the cold gray dusk and made the snow look whiter. The bitter weather had driven every one indoors and Ethan had the long rural street to himself. Suddenly he heard the brisk play of sleigh-bells and a cutter passed him, drawn by a free-going horse. Ethan recognized Michael Eady's roan colt, and young Denis Eady, in a handsome new fur cap, leaned forward and waved a greeting. "Hello, Ethe!" he shouted and spun on.

The cutter was going in the direction of the Frome farm, and Ethan's heart contracted as he listened to the dwindling bells. What more likely than that Denis Eady had heard of Zeena's departure for Bettsbridge, and was profiting by the opportunity to spend an hour with Mattie? Ethan was ashamed of the storm of jealousy in his breast. It seemed unworthy of the girl that his thoughts of her should be so violent.

He walked on to the church corner and entered the shade of the Varnum spruces, where he had stood with her the night before. As he passed into their gloom he saw an indistinct outline just ahead of him. At his approach it melted for an instant into two separate shapes and then conjoined again, and he heard a kiss, and a half-laughing "Oh!" provoked by the discovery of his presence. Again the outline hastily disunited and the Varnum gate slammed on one half while the other

hurried on ahead of him. Ethan smiled at the discomfiture he had caused. What did it matter to Ned Hale and Ruth Varnum if they were caught kissing each other? Everybody in Starkfield knew they were engaged. It pleased Ethan to have surprised a pair of lovers on the spot where he and Mattie had stood with such a sense of nearness in their hearts; but he felt a pang at the thought that these two need not hide their happiness.

He fetched the grays from Hale's stable and started on his long climb back to the farm. The cold was less sharp than earlier in the day and a thick fleecy sky threatened snow for the morrow. Here and there a star pricked through, showing behind it a deep well of blue. In an hour or two the moon would push up over the ridge behind the farm, burn a gold-edged rent in the clouds, and then be swallowed by them. A mournful peace hung on the fields, as though they felt the relaxing grasp of the cold and stretched themselves in their winter sleep.

Ethan's ears were alert for the jingle of sleigh-bells, but not a sound broke the silence of the lonely road. As he drew near the farm he saw, through the thin screen of larches at the gate, a light twinkling in the house above him. "She's up in her room," he said to himself, "fixing herself up for supper"; and he remembered Zeena's sarcastic stare when Mattie, on the evening of her arrival, had come down to supper with smoothed hair and a ribbon at her neck.

He passed by the graves on the knoll and turned his head to glance at one of the older head-stones, which had interested him deeply as a boy because it bore his name.

SACRED TO THE MEMORY OF
ETHAN FROME AND ENDURANCE HIS WIFE,
WHO DWELLED TOGETHER IN PEACE
FOR FIFTY YEARS.

He used to think that fifty years sounded like a long time to live together; but now it seemed to him that they might pass in a flash. Then, with a sudden dart of irony, he wondered if, when their turn came, the same epitaph would be written over him and Zeena. **[322/323]**

He opened the barn-door and craned his head into the obscurity, half-fearing to discover Denis Eady's roan colt in the stall beside the sorrel. But the old horse was there alone, mumbling his crib with toothless jaws, and Ethan whistled cheerfully while he bedded down the grays and shook an extra measure of oats into their mangers. His was not a tuneful throat, but harsh melodies burst from it as he locked the barn and sprang up the hill to the house. He reached the kitchen-porch and turned the door-handle; but the door did not yield to his touch.

Startled at finding it locked he rattled the handle violently; then he reflected that Mattie was alone and that it was natural she should shut herself in at twilight. He stood in the darkness expecting to hear her step. It did not come, and after vainly straining his ears he called out in a voice that shook with joy: "Hello, Matt!"

Silence answered; but in a minute or two he caught a sound on the stairs and saw a line of light about the door-frame, as he had seen it the night before. So strange was the precision with which the incidents of the previous evening were repeating themselves that he half expected, when he heard the key turn, to see his wife before him on the threshold; but the door opened, and it was Mattie who stood there.

She stood just as Zeena had stood, a lifted lamp in her hand, against the black background of the kitchen. She held the light at the same level, and it drew out with the same distinctness her slim young throat and the brown wrist no bigger than a child's. Then, striking upward, it threw a lustrous fleck on her lips, edged her eyes with velvet shadow, and laid a warm whiteness above the black curve of her brows.

She wore her usual dress of dark stuff, and there was no bow at her neck; but

through her hair she had run a streak of crimson ribbon. This tribute to the unusual transformed and glorified her. She seemed to Ethan taller, fuller, more womanly in shape and motion. She stood aside, smiling silently, while he entered, and then moved away from him with something soft and flowing in her gait. She set the lamp on the table, and he saw that it was carefully laid for supper, with fresh dough-nuts, stewed blueberries and his favourite pickles in a dish of gay red glass. A bright fire glowed in the stove, and the cat lay stretched before it, watching the table with a drowsy eye.

Ethan was suffocated with the sense of well-being. He went out into the passage to hang up his coat and pull off his wet boots. When he came back Mattie had set the teapot on the table and the cat was rubbing itself persuasively against her ankles.

"Why, Puss! I nearly tripped over you," she exclaimed, her eyes all laughter.

Again Ethan felt a sudden twinge of jealousy. Could it be his coming that gave her such a kindled face?

"Well, Matt, any visitors?" he threw off, stooping down carelessly to examine the fastening of the stove.

She nodded and laughed. "Yes, one," and he felt a blackness settling on his brows.

"Who was that?" he questioned, raising himself up to slant a glance at her beneath his scowl.

Her eyes danced with malice. "Why, Jotham Powell. He came in after he got back, and asked for a drop of coffee before he went down home."

The blackness lifted and light flooded Ethan's brain. "That all? Well, I hope you made out to let him have it." And after a pause he felt it right to add: "I suppose he got Zeena over to the Flats all right?"

"Oh, yes; in plenty of time."

The name threw a chill between them, and they stood a moment looking sideways at each other before Mattie said with a shy laugh: "I guess it's about time for supper."

They drew their seats up to the table, and the cat, unbidden, jumped between them onto Zeena's chair. "Oh, Puss!" said Mattie, and they laughed again.

Ethan, a moment earlier, had felt himself on the brink of eloquence; but the mention of Zeena had paralyzed him. Mattie seemed to feel the contagion of his embarrassment, and sat with downcast eyes, sipping her tea, while he feigned an insatiable appetite for doughnuts and pickles. At last, after casting about for an effective opening, he took a long gulp of tea, cleared his throat, and said: "Looks as if there'd be more snow."

She feigned great interest. "Is that so? Do you suppose it'll interfere with Zeena's [323/324] getting back?" She flushed red as the question escaped her, and hastily set down the cup she was lifting.

Ethan reached over for another helping of pickles. "You never can tell, this time of year, it drifts so bad on the Flats." The name had benumbed him again, and once more he felt as if Zeena were in the room between them.

"Oh, Puss, you're too greedy!" Mattie cried.

The cat, unnoticed, had crept up on muffled paws from Zeena's seat to the table, and was stealthily elongating its body in the direction of the milk-jug, which stood between Ethan and Mattie. The two leaned forward at the same moment and their hands met on the handle of the jug. Mattie's hand was underneath, and Ethan kept his clasped on it a moment longer than was necessary. The cat, profiting by this unusual demonstration, tried to effect an unnoticed retreat, and in doing so backed into the pickle dish, which fell to the floor with a crash.

Mattie, in an instant, had sprung from her chair and was down on her knees by the fragments.

"Oh, Ethan, Ethan—it's all to pieces! What will Zeena say?"

But this time his courage was up. "Well, she'll have to say it to the cat, any way!" he rejoined with a laugh, kneeling down at Mattie's side to scrape up the swimming pickles.

She lifted stricken eyes to him. "Yes, but, you see, she never meant it should be used, not even when there was company; and I had to get up on the stepladder to reach it down from the top shelf of the china-closet, where she keeps it with all her best things, and of course she'll want to know why I did it——"

The case was so serious that it called forth all of Ethan's latent resolution.

"She needn't know anything about it if you keep quiet. I'll get another just like it to-morrow. Where did it come from? I'll go to Shadd's Falls for it if I have to!"

"Oh, you'll never get another even there! It was a wedding present—don't you remember? It came all the way from Philadelphia, from Zeena's aunt that married the minister. That's why she wouldn't ever use it. Oh, Ethan, Ethan, what in the world shall I do?"

She began to cry, and he felt as if every one of her tears were pouring over him like burning lead. "Don't, Matt, don't—oh, don't!" he implored her.

She struggled to her feet, and he rose and followed her helplessly while she spread out the pieces of glass on the kitchen dresser. It seemed to him as if the shattered fragments of their evening lay there.

"Here, give them to me," he said in a voice of sudden authority.

She drew aside, instinctively obeying his tone. "Oh, Ethan, what are you going to do with it?"

Without replying he gathered the pieces of glass into his broad palm and walked out of the kitchen to the passage. There he lit a candle-end, opened the china-closet, and, reaching his long arm up to the highest shelf, laid the pieces together with such accuracy of touch that a close inspection convinced him of the impossibility of detecting from below that the dish was broken. If he glued it together the next morning months might elapse before his wife noticed what had happened, and meanwhile he might after all be able to match the dish at Shadd's Falls or Bettsbridge. Having satisfied himself that there was no risk of immediate discovery he went back to the kitchen with a lighter step, and found Mattie disconsolately removing the last scraps of pickle from the floor.

"It's all right, Matt. Come back and finish supper," he commanded her.

Completely reassured, she shone on him through tear-hung lashes, and his soul swelled with pride as he saw how his tone subdued her. She did not even ask what he had done. Except when he was steering a big log down the mountain to his mill he had never known such a thrilling sense of mastery.

V

They finished supper, and while Mattie cleared the table Ethan went to look at the cows and then took a last turn about the house. The earth lay dark under a muffled sky and the air was so still that now and then he heard a lump of snow come thumping down from a tree far off on the edge of the wood-lot.

When he returned to the kitchen Mattie had pushed up his chair to the stove and seated herself near the lamp with a bit of [**324/325**] sewing. The scene was just what his morning vision had shown him. He sat down, drew his pipe from his pocket and stretched his feet to the glow. His hard day's work in the keen air made him feel at once lazy and light of mood, and he had a confused sense of being in another world, where all was warmth and harmony and time could bring no change. The only drawback to his complete well-being was the fact that he could not see Mattie from where he sat; but he was too indolent to move and after a moment he said: "Come over here and sit by the stove."

Zeena's empty rocking-chair stood opposite him. Mattie rose obediently, and seated herself in it. Seeing her young brown head against the chintz cushion that habitually framed his wife's gaunt countenance, Ethan had a momentary shock. It was almost as if the other face, the face of the superseded woman, had obliterated that of the intruder. After a moment Mattie seemed to be affected by the same sense of constraint. She changed her position, leaning forward to bend her head above her work, so that he saw only the foreshortened tip of her nose and the streak of red in her hair; then she slipped to her feet, saying, "I can't see to sew," and went back to her chair by the lamp.

Ethan made a pretext of getting up to replenish the stove, and when he returned to his seat he pushed it sideways that he might get a view of her profile and of the lamplight falling on her hands. The cat, who had been a puzzled observer of these unusual movements, jumped up into Zeena's chair, rolled itself into a ball, and lay watching them with narrowed eyes.

Deep quiet sank on the room. The clock ticked above the dresser, a piece of charred wood fell now and then in the stove, and a faint sharp scent from the geraniums mingled with the odour of Ethan's smoke, which began to throw a blue haze about the lamp and to hang like cobwebs in the shadowy corners of the room.

All constraint had vanished between the two, and they began to talk easily and simply. They spoke of every-day things, of the prospect of snow, of the next church sociable, of the loves and quarrels of Starkfield. The commonplace nature of what they said produced in Ethan an illusion of long-established intimacy which no outburst of emotion could have given, and he set his imagination adrift on the fiction that they had always spent their evenings thus and would always go on doing so . . .

"This is the night we were to have gone coasting, Matt," he said at length, with the rich sense, as he spoke, that they could go on any other night they chose, since they had all time before them.

She smiled back at him. "I guess you forgot!"

"No, I didn't forget; but it's as dark as

Egypt out-doors. We might go to-morrow if there's a moon."

She laughed with pleasure, and the lamplight sparkled on her lips and teeth. "That would be lovely, Ethan!"

He kept his eyes fixed on her, wondering at the way her face changed with each turn of their talk, like a wheat-field under the breeze. It was intoxicating to find such magic in his clumsy words, and he longed to try new ways of using it.

"Would you be scared to go down the Corbury road with me on a night like this?" he asked.

Her cheeks burned redder. "I ain't any more scared than you are!"

"Well, *I'd* be scared, then; I wouldn't do it. That's an ugly corner down by the big elm. If a fellow didn't keep his eyes open he'd go plumb into it." He luxuriated in the sense of protection and authority which his words conveyed. To prolong and intensify the feeling he added: "I guess we're well enough here."

She let her lids sink slowly, in the way he loved. "Yes, we're well enough here," she sighed.

Her tone was so sweet that he took the pipe from his mouth and drew his chair up to the table. Leaning forward, he touched the farther end of the strip of brown stuff that she was hemming. "Say, Matt," he began with a smile, "what do you think I saw under the Varnum spruces, coming along home just now? I saw a friend of yours getting kissed."

The words had been on his tongue all the evening, but now that he had spoken them they struck him as inexpressibly vulgar and out-of-place.

Mattie blushed to the roots of her hair and pulled her needle rapidly twice or thrice through her work, insensibly drawing the end of it away from him. "I sup-[325/326]pose it was Ruth and Ned," she said in a low voice, as though he had suddenly touched on something grave.

Ethan had imagined that his allusion might open the way to the accepted pleasantries, and these perhaps in turn to a harmless caress, if only a mere touch on her hand. But now he felt as if her blush had set a flaming guard about her. He supposed it was his natural awkwardness that made him feel so. He knew that most young men made nothing at all of giving a pretty girl a kiss, and he remembered that the night before, when he had put his arm about Mattie, she had not resisted. But that had been out of doors, under the open irresponsible night. Now, in the warm lamplit room, with all its ancient implications of conformity and order, she seemed infinitely farther away from him and more unapproachable.

To ease his constraint he said: "I suppose they'll be setting a date before long."

"Yes. I shouldn't wonder if they got married some time along in the summer." She pronounced the word *married* as if her voice caressed it. It seemed a rustling covert leading to enchanted glades. A pang shot through Ethan, and he said, twisting away from her in his chair: "It'll be your turn next, I wouldn't wonder."

She laughed a little uncertainly. "Why do you keep on saying that?"

He echoed her laugh. "I guess I do it to get used to the idea."

He drew up to the table again and she sewed on in silence, with dropped lashes, while he sat in fascinated contemplation of the way in which her hands went up and down above the strip of stuff, just as he had seen a pair of birds make short perpendicular flights over a nest they were building. At length, without turning her head or lifting her lids, she said in a low tone: "It's not because you think Zeena's got anything against me, is it?"

His former dread started up full-armed at the suggestion. "Why, what do you mean?" he stammered.

She raised distressed eyes to his, her work dropping on the table between them. "I don't know. I thought last night she seemed to have."

"I'd like to know what," he growled.

"Nobody can tell with Zeena." It was the first time they had ever spoken so openly of her attitude toward Mattie, and the repetition of the name seemed to carry it to the farther corners of the room and send it back to them in long repercussions of sound. Mattie waited, as if to let the echo drop, and then went on: "She hasn't said anything to *you?*"

He shook his head. "No, not a word."

She tossed the hair back from her forehead with a laugh. "I guess I'm just nervous then. I'm not going to think about it any more."

"Oh, no—don't let's think about it, Matt!"

The sudden heat of his tone made her colour mount again, not with a rush, but gradually, delicately, like the reflection of a thought stealing slowly across her heart. She sat silent, her hands clasped on her work, and it seemed to him that a warm current flowed toward him along the strip of stuff that still lay unrolled between them. Cautiously he slid his hand palm-downward along the table till his finger-tips touched the end of the stuff. A faint vibration of her lashes seemed to show that she was aware of his gesture, and that it had sent a counter-current running back to her; and she let her hands lie motionless on the other end of the strip.

As they sat thus he heard a sound behind him and turned his head. The cat had jumped from Zeena's chair to dart at a mouse in the wainscot, and as a result of the violent movement the empty chair had set up a spectral rocking.

"She'll be rocking in it herself this time to-morrow," Ethan thought. "I've been in a dream, and this is the only evening we'll ever have together."

The return to reality was as painful as the return to consciousness after taking an anæsthetic. His body and brain ached with indescribable weariness, and he could think of nothing to say or to do that should arrest the mad flight of the moments.

His alteration of mood seemed to have communicated itself to Mattie. She looked up at him languidly, as though her lids were weighted with sleep and it cost her an effort to raise them. Her glance fell on his hand, which now completely covered the end of her work and grasped it as if it were a part of herself. He saw a scarcely perceptible tremor cross her face, and without knowing what he did he stooped his head [**326/327**] and kissed the bit of stuff in his hold. As his lips rested on it he felt it glide slowly from beneath them, and saw that Mattie had risen and was silently rolling up her work. She fastened it with a pin, and then, finding her thimble and scissors, put them, with the roll of stuff, into the box covered with fancy paper which he had once brought to her from Bettsbridge.

He stood up also, looking vaguely about the room. The clock above the dresser struck eleven.

"Is the fire all right?" she asked in a low voice.

He opened the door of the stove and poked aimlessly at the embers. When he raised himself again he saw that she was dragging toward the stove the old soapbox lined with carpet in which the cat made its bed. Then she recrossed the floor and lifted two of the geranium pots in her arms, moving them away from the cold window. He followed her and brought the other geraniums, the hyacinth bulbs in a cracked custard bowl and the German ivy trained over an old croquet hoop.

When these nightly duties were performed there was nothing left to do but to bring in the tin candlestick from the passage, light the candle and blow out the lamp. Ethan put the candlestick in Mattie's hand and she went out of the kitchen ahead of him, the light that she carried before her making her dark hair look like a drift of mist on the moon.

"Good-night, Matt," he said as she put her foot on the first step of the stairs.

She turned and looked at him a moment. "Good night, Ethan," she answered, and went up.

When the door of her room had closed

on her he remembered that he had not even touched her hand.

VI

The next morning at breakfast Jotham Powell was between them, and Ethan tried to hide his joy under an air of exaggerated indifference, lounging back in his chair to throw scraps to the cat, growling at the weather, and not so much as offering to help Mattie when she rose to clear away the dishes.

He did not know why he was so irrationally happy, for nothing was changed in his life or hers. He had not even touched the tip of her fingers or looked her full in the eyes. But their evening together had given him a vision of what life at her side might be, and he was glad now that he had done nothing to trouble the sweetness of the picture. He had a fancy that she knew what had restrained him . . .

There was a last load of lumber to be hauled to the village, and Jotham Powell—who did not work regularly for Ethan in winter—had "come round" to help with the job. But a wet snow, melting to sleet, had fallen in the night and turned the snowy roads to glass. There was more wet in the air and it seemed likely to both men that the weather would "milden" toward afternoon and make the going safer. Ethan therefore proposed to his assistant that they should load the sledge at the wood-lot, as they had done on the previous morning, and put off the "teaming" to Starkfield till later in the day. This plan had the advantage of enabling him to send Jotham to the Flats after dinner to meet Zenobia, while he himself took the lumber down to the village.

He told Jotham to go out and harness up the grays, and for a moment he and Mattie had the kitchen to themselves. She had plunged the breakfast dishes into a tin dish-pan and was bending above it with her slim arms bared to the elbow, the steam from the hot water beading her forehead and tightening her rough hair into little brown rings like the tendrils on the traveller's joy.

Ethan stood looking at her, his heart in his throat. He wanted to say: "We shall never be alone again like this." Instead, he reached down his tobacco-pouch from a shelf of the dresser, put it into his pocket and said: "I guess I can make out to be home for dinner."

She answered "All right, Ethan," and he heard her singing over the dishes as he went.

As soon as the sledge was loaded he meant to send Jotham back to the farm and hurry on foot into the village to buy the glue for the pickle-dish. With ordinary luck he should have had time to carry out this plan; but everything went wrong from the start. On the way over to the wood-lot one of the grays slipped on a glare of ice and cut his knee; and when they got [**327/328**] him up again Jotham had to go back to the barn for a strip of rag to bind the cut. Then, when the loading finally began, a sleety rain was coming down once more, and the tree-trunks were so slippery that it took twice as long as usual to lift them and get them in place on the sledge. It was what Jotham called a sour morning for work, and the horses, shivering and stamping under their wet blankets, seemed to like it as little as the men. It was long past the dinner hour when the job was done, and Ethan had to give up going to the village because he wanted to lead the injured horse home and wash the cut himself.

He thought that by starting out again with the lumber as soon as he had finished his dinner he might get back to the farm with the glue before Jotham and the old sorrel had had time to fetch Zenobia from the Flats; but he knew the chance was a slight one. It turned on the state of the roads and on the possible lateness of the Bettsbridge train. He remembered afterward, with a grim flash of self-derision, what importance he had attached to the weighing of these probabilities . . .

As soon as dinner was over he set out again for the wood-lot, not daring to linger till Jotham Powell left. The hired man was still drying his wet feet at the stove, and Ethan could only give Mattie a quick look as he said beneath his breath: "I'll be back early."

He fancied that she nodded her comprehension; and with that scant solace he had to trudge off through the rain.

He had driven his load half-way to the village when Jotham Powell overtook him, urging the reluctant sorrel toward the Flats. "I'll have to hurry up to do it," Ethan mused, as the sleigh dropped down ahead of him over the dip of the school house hill. He worked like ten at the unloading, and when it was over hastened on to Michael Eady's for the glue. Eady and his assistant were both "down street," and young Denis, who seldom deigned to take their place, was lounging by the stove with some of the golden youth of Starkfield. They hailed Ethan with ironic compliment and offers of conviviality; but no one knew where to find the glue. Ethan, consumed with the longing for a last moment alone with Mattie, hung about impatiently while Denis made an ineffectual search in the obscurer corners of the store. "Looks as if we were all sold out. But if you'll wait around till the old man comes along maybe he can put his hand on it."

"I'm obliged to you, but I'll try if I can get it down at Mrs. Homan's," Ethan answered, burning to be gone.

Denis's commercial instinct compelled him to aver on oath that what Eady's store could not produce would never be found at the widow Homan's; but Ethan, heedless of this boast, had already climbed to the sledge and was driving on to the rival establishment. Here, after considerable search, and sympathetic questions as to what he wanted it for, and whether ordinary flour paste wouldn't do as well if she couldn't find it, the widow Homan finally hunted down her solitary bottle of glue to its hiding-place in a medley of cough-lozenges and corset-laces.

"I hope Zeena ain't broken anything she sets store by," she called after him as he turned the grays toward home.

The fitful bursts of sleet had changed into a persistent rain and the horses had heavy work even without a load behind them. Once or twice, hearing sleigh-bells, Ethan turned his head, fancying that Zeena and Jotham might overtake him; but the old sorrel was not in sight, and he set his face against the rain and urged on his ponderous pair.

The barn was empty when the horses turned into it and, after giving them the most perfunctory ministrations they had ever received from him, he strode up to the house and pushed open the kitchen door.

Mattie was there alone, as he had pictured her. She was bending over a pan on the stove; but at the sound of his step she turned with a start and sprang to him.

"See here, Matt, I've got some stuff to mend the dish with! Let me get at it quick," he cried, waving the bottle in one hand while he put her lightly aside with the other; but she did not seem to hear him.

"Oh, Ethan—Zeena's come," she said in a whisper, clutching his sleeve.

They stood and stared at each other, pale as culprits.

"But the sorrel's not in the barn!" Ethan stammered. **[328/329]**

"Jotham Powell brought some goods over from the Flats for his wife, and he drove right on with them," she explained.

He gazed blankly about the kitchen, which looked cold and squalid in the rainy winter twilight.

"How is she?" he asked, dropping his voice to Mattie's whisper.

She looked away from him uncertainly. "I don't know. She went right up to her room."

"She didn't say anything?"

"No."

Ethan sent out his doubts in a low

whistle and thrust the bottle back into his pocket. "Don't fret; I'll come down and mend it in the night," he said. He pulled on his wet coat again and went back to the barn to feed the grays.

While he was there Jotham Powell drove up with the sleigh, and when the horses had been attended to Ethan said to him: "You might as well come back up for a bite." He was not sorry to assure himself of Jotham's neutralizing presence at the supper table, for Zeena was always "nervous" after a journey. But the hired man, though seldom loth to accept a meal not included in his wages, opened his stiff jaws to answer slowly: "I'm obliged to you, but I guess I'll go along back."

Ethan looked at him in surprise. "Better come up and dry off. Looks as if there'd be something hot for supper."

Jotham's facial muscles were unmoved by this appeal and, his vocabulary being limited, he merely repeated: "I guess I'll go along back."

To Ethan there was something vaguely ominous in this stolid rejection of free food and warmth, and he wondered what had happened on the drive to nerve Jotham to such stoicism. Perhaps Zeena had failed to see the new doctor or had not liked his counsels: Ethan knew that in such cases the first person she met was likely to be held responsible for her grievance.

When he re-entered the kitchen the lamp lit up the same scene of shining comfort as on the previous evening. The table had been as carefully laid, a clear fire glowed in the stove, the cat dozed in its warmth, and Mattie came forward carrying a plate of dough-nuts.

She and Ethan looked at each other in silence; then she said, as she had said the night before: "I guess it's about time for supper."

VII

Ethan went out into the passage to hang up his wet garments. He listened for Zeena's step and, not hearing it, called her name up the stairs. She did not answer, and after a moment's hesitation he went up and opened her door. The room was almost dark, but in the obscurity he saw her sitting by the window, bolt upright, and knew by the rigidity of the outline projected against the pane that she had not taken off her travelling dress.

"Well, Zeena," he ventured from the threshold.

She did not move, and he continued: "Supper's about ready. Ain't you coming?"

She replied: "I don't feel as if I could touch a morsel."

It was the consecrated formula, and he expected it to be followed, as usual, by her rising and going down to supper. But she remained seated, and he could think of nothing more felicitous than: "I presume you're tired after the long ride."

Turning her head at this, she answered solemnly: "I'm a great deal sicker than you think."

Her words fell on his ear with a strange shock of wonder. He had often heard her pronounce them before—what if at last they were true?

He advanced a step or two into the dim room. "I hope that's not so, Zeena," he said.

She continued to gaze at him through the twilight with a mien of wan authority, as of one consciously singled out for a great fate. "I've got complications," she said.

Ethan knew the word for one of exceptional import. Almost everybody in the neighbourhood had "troubles," frankly localized and specified; but only the chosen had "complications." To have them was in itself a distinction, though it was also, in most cases, a death-warrant. People struggled on for years with "troubles," but they almost always succumbed to "complications."

Ethan's heart was jerking to and fro between two extremities of feeling, but for the moment compassion prevailed.

His wife [**329/330**] looked so hard and lonely, sitting there in the darkness with such thoughts.

"Is that what the new doctor told you?" he asked, instinctively lowering his voice.

"Yes. He says any regular doctor would want me to have an operation."

Ethan was aware that, in regard to the important question of surgical intervention, the female opinion of the neighbourhood was divided, some glorying in the prestige conferred by operations while others shunned them as indelicate. Ethan, from motives of economy, had always been glad that Zeena was of the latter faction.

In the agitation caused by the gravity of her announcement he sought a consolatory short cut. "What do you know about this doctor anyway? Nobody ever told you that before."

He saw his blunder before she could take it up: she wanted sympathy, not consolation.

"I didn't need to have anybody tell me I was losing ground every day. Everybody but you could see it. And everybody in Bettsbridge knows about Dr. Buck. He has his office in Worcester, and comes over once a fortnight to Shadd's Falls and Bettsbridge for consultations. Eliza Spears was wasting away with kidney trouble before she went to him, and now she's up and around, and singing in the choir."

"Well, I'm glad of that. You must do just what he tells you," Ethan answered sympathetically.

She was still looking at him. "I mean to," she said. He was struck by a new note in her voice. It was neither whining nor reproachful, but drily resolute.

"What does he want you should do?" he asked, with a mounting vision of fresh expenses.

"He wants I should have a hired girl. He says I oughtn't to have to do a single thing around the house."

"A hired girl?" Ethan stood transfixed.

"Yes. And Aunt Martha found me one right off. Everybody said I was lucky to get a girl to come away out here, and I agreed to give her a dollar extry to make sure. She'll be over to-morrow afternoon."

Wrath and dismay contended in Ethan. He had foreseen an immediate demand for money but not a permanent drain on his scant resources. He no longer believed what Zeena had told him of the supposed seriousness of her state: he saw in her expedition to Bettsbridge only a plot hatched between herself and her Pierce relations to foist on him the cost of a servant; and for the moment wrath predominated.

"If you meant to engage a girl you ought to have told me before you started," he said.

"How could I tell you before I started? How did I know what Dr. Buck would say?"

"Oh, Dr. Buck—" Ethan's incredulity escaped in a short laugh. "Did Dr. Buck tell you how I was to pay her wages?"

Her voice rose furiously with his. "No, he didn't. For I'd 'a' been ashamed to tell *him* that you grudged me the money to get back my health, when I lost it nursing your own mother!"

"*You* lost your health nursing mother?"

"Yes; and my folks all told me at the time you couldn't do no less than marry me after——"

"Zeena!"

Through the obscurity which hid their faces their thoughts seemed to dart at each other like serpents shooting venom. Ethan was seized with horror of the scene and shame at his own share in it. It was as senseless and savage as a physical fight between two enemies in the darkness.

He turned to the shelf above the chimney, groped for matches and lit the one candle in the room. At first its weak flame made no impression on the shadows; then Zeena's face stood grimly out against the uncurtained pane, which had turned from gray to black.

It was the first scene of open anger between the couple in their sad seven years together, and Ethan felt as if he had lost an irretrievable advantage in descending to the level of recrimination. But the practical problem was there and had to be dealt with.

"You know I haven't got the money to pay for a girl, Zeena. You'll have to send her back: I can't do it."

"The doctor says it'll be my death if I go on slaving the way I've had to. He doesn't understand how I've stood it as long as I have."

"Slaving!—" He checked himself again. "You sha'n't lift a hand, if he says so. I'll do everything round the house my-self——"

She broke in: "You're neglecting the farm enough already," and this being true, [330/331] he found no answer, and left her time to add ironically: "Better send me over to the almshouse and done with it. I guess there's been Fromes there afore now."

The taunt burned into him, but he let it pass. "I haven't got the money. That settles it."

There was a moment's pause in the struggle, as though the combatants were testing their weapons. Then Zeena said in a level voice: "I thought you were to get fifty dollars from Andrew Hale for that lumber."

"Andrew Hale never pays under three months." He had hardly spoken when he remembered the excuse he had made for not accompanying his wife to the station the day before; and the blood rose to his frowning brows.

"Why, you told me yesterday you'd fixed it up with him to pay cash down. You said that was why you couldn't drive me over to the Flats."

Ethan had no suppleness in deceiv-ing. He had never before been convicted of a lie, and all the recourses of evasion failed him. "I guess that was a misunder-standing," he stammered.

"You ain't got the money?"

"No."

"And you ain't going to get it?"

"No."

"Well, I couldn't know that when I engaged the girl, could I?"

"No." He paused to control his voice. "But you know it now. I'm sorry, but it can't be helped. You're a poor man's wife, Zeena; but I'll do the best I can for you."

For awhile she sat motionless, as if re-flecting, her arms stretched along the arms of her chair, her eyes fixed on va-cancy. "Oh, I guess we'll make out," she said mildly.

The change in her tone reassured him. "Of course we will! There's a whole lot more I can do for you, and Mattie——"

Zeena, while he spoke, seemed to be following out some elaborate mental cal-culation. She emerged from it to say: "There'll be Mattie's board less, any-how——"

Ethan, supposing the discussion to be over, had turned to go down to supper. He stopped short, not grasping what he heard. "Mattie's board less—?" he be-gan.

Zeena laughed. It was an odd unfamil-iar sound—he did not remember ever having heard her laugh before. "You didn't suppose I was going to keep two girls, did you? No wonder you were scared at the expense!"

He still had but a confused sense of what she was saying. From the beginning of the discussion he had instinctively avoided the mention of Mattie's name, fearing he hardly knew what: criticism, complaints, or vague allusions to the im-minent probability of her marrying. But the thought of a definite rupture had never come to him, and even now could not lodge itself in his mind.

"I don't know what you mean," he said. "Mattie Silver's not a hired girl. She's your relation."

"She's a pauper that's hung onto us all after her father'd done his best to ruin us. I've kep' her here a whole year: it's somebody else's turn now."

As the shrill words shot out Ethan heard a tap on the door, which he had drawn shut when he turned back from the threshold.

"Ethan—Zeena!" Mattie's voice sounded gaily from the landing, "do you know what time it is? Supper's been ready half an hour."

Inside the room there was a moment's silence; then Zeena called out from her seat: "I'm not coming down to supper."

"Oh, I'm sorry! Aren't you well? Sha'n't I bring you up a bite of something?"

Ethan roused himself with an effort and opened the door. "Go along down, Matt. Zeena's just a little tired. I'm coming."

He heard her "All right!" and her quick step on the stairs; then he shut the door and turned back into the room. His wife's attitude was unchanged, her face inexorable, and he was seized with the despairing sense of his helplessness.

"You ain't going to do it, Zeena?"

"Do what?" she emitted between flattened lips.

"Send Mattie away—like this?"

"I never bargained to take her for life!"

He continued with rising vehemence: "You can't put her out of the house like a thief—a poor girl without friends or money. She's done her best for you and she's got no place to go to. You may forget she's your kin but everybody else'll remember it. If you do a thing like that what do you suppose folks'll say of you?"

Zeena waited a moment, as if giving him time to feel the full force of the contrast be- [331/332] tween his own excitement and her composure. Then she replied in the same smooth voice: "I know well enough what they say of my having kep' her here as long as I have."

Ethan's hand dropped from the doorknob, which he had held clenched since he had drawn the door shut on Mattie. His wife's retort was like a knife-cut across the sinews and he felt suddenly weak and powerless. He had meant to humble himself, to argue that Mattie's keep didn't cost much, after all, that he

could make out to buy a stove and fix up a place in the attic for the hired girl—but Zeena's words revealed the peril of such pleadings.

"You mean to tell her she's got to go—at once?" he faltered out, in terror of letting his wife complete her sentence.

As if trying to make him see reason she replied impartially; "The girl will be over from Bettsbridge to-morrow, and I presume she's got to have somewheres to sleep."

Ethan looked at her with loathing. She was no longer the listless creature who had lived at his side in a state of sullen self-absorption, but a mysterious alien presence, an evil energy secreted from the long years of silent brooding. It was the sense of his helplessness that sharpened his antipathy. There had never been anything in her that one could appeal to; but as long as he could ignore and command he had remained indifferent. Now she had mastered him and he abhorred her. Mattie was her relation, not his: there were no means by which he could compel her to keep the girl under her roof. All the long misery of his baffled past, of his youth of failure, hardship and vain effort, rose up in his soul in bitterness and seemed to take shape before him in the woman who, at every turn, had barred his way. She had taken everything else from him; and now she meant to take the one thing that made up for all the others. For a moment such a flame of hate rose in him that it ran down his arm and clenched his fist against her. He took a wild step forward and then stopped.

"You're—you're not coming down?" he said in a bewildered voice.

"No. I guess I'll lay down on the bed a little while," she answered mildly; and he turned and walked out of the room.

In the kitchen Mattie was sitting by the stove, the cat curled up on her knees. She sprang to her feet as Ethan entered and carried the covered dish of meat-pie to the table.

"I hope Zeena isn't sick?" she asked.

"No."

She shone at him across the table. "Well, sit right down then. You must be starving." She uncovered the pie and pushed it over to him. So they were to have one more evening together, her happy eyes seemed to say!

He helped himself mechanically and began to eat; then disgust took him by the throat, and he laid down his fork.

Mattie's tender gaze was on him and she marked the gesture.

"Why, Ethan, what's the matter? Don't it taste right?"

"Yes—it's first-rate. Only I—" He pushed his plate away, rose from his chair, and walked around the table to her side. She started up with frightened eyes.

"Ethan, there's something wrong! I _knew_ there was!"

She seemed to melt against him in her terror, and he caught her in his arms, held her fast there, felt her lashes beat his cheek like netted butterflies.

"What is it—what is it?" she stammered; but he had found her lips and was drinking unconsciousness of everything but the joy they gave him.

She lingered a moment, caught in the same strong current; then she slipped from him and drew back a step or two, pale and troubled. Her look smote him with compunction, and he cried out, as if he saw her drowning in a dream: "You can't go, Matt! I'll never let you!"

"Go—go?" she stammered. "Must I go?"

The words went on sounding between them as though a torch of warning flew from hand to hand through a black landscape.

Ethan was overcome with shame at his lack of self-control in flinging the news at her so brutally. His head reeled and he had to support himself against the table. All the while he felt as if he were still kissing her, and yet dying of thirst for her lips.

"Ethan, what has happened? Is Zeena mad with me?"

Her cry steadied him, though it deep-ened his wrath and pity. "No, no," he assured [**332/333**] her, "it's not that. But this new doctor has scared her about herself. You know she believes all they say the first time she sees them. And this one's told her she won't get well unless she lays up and don't do a thing about the house—not for months——"

He paused, his eyes wandering from her miserably. She stood silent a moment, drooping before him like a broken branch. She was so small and weak-looking that it wrung his heart; but suddenly she lifted her head and looked straight at him. "And she wants somebody handier in my place? Is that it?"

"That's what she says to-night."

"If she says it to-night she'll say it to-morrow."

Both bowed to the inexorable truth: they knew that Zeena never changed her mind, and that in her case a resolve once taken was equivalent to an act performed.

There was a long silence between them; then Mattie said in a low voice: "Don't be too sorry, Ethan."

"Oh, God—oh, God," he groaned. The glow of passion he had felt for her had melted to an aching tenderness. He saw her quick lids beating back the tears, and longed to take her in his arms and soothe her.

"You're letting your supper get cold," she admonished him with a pale gleam of gaiety.

"Oh, Matt—Matt—where'll you go to?"

Her lids sank and a tremor crossed her face. He saw that for the first time the thought of the future came to her distinctly. "I might get something to do over at Stamford," she faltered, as if knowing that he knew she had no hope.

He dropped back into his seat and hid his face in his hands. Despair seized him at the thought of her setting out alone to renew the weary quest for work. In the only place where she was known she was surrounded by indifference or animosity; and what chance had she, inexperienced and untrained, among the million bread-seekers of the cities? There came back to him miserable tales he had heard at Worcester, and the faces of girls whose lives had begun as hopefully as Mattie's. . . It was not possible to think of such things without a revolt of his whole being. He sprang up suddenly.

"You can't go, Matt! I won't let you! She's always had her way, but I mean to have mine now——"

Mattie lifted her hand with a quick gesture, and he heard his wife's step behind him.

Zeena came into the room with her dragging down-at-the-heel step, and quietly took her accustomed seat between them.

"I felt a little mite better, and Dr. Buck says I ought to eat all I can to keep my stren'th up, even if I ain't got any appetite," she said in her flat whine, reaching across Mattie for the teapot. Her "good" dress had been replaced by the black calico and brown knitted shawl which formed her daily wear, and with them she had put on her usual face and manner. She poured out her tea, added a great deal of milk to it, helped herself largely to pie and pickles, and made the familiar gesture of adjusting her false teeth before she began to eat. The cat rubbed itself ingratiatingly against her, and she said "Good Pussy," stooped to stroke it and gave it a scrap of meat from her plate.

Ethan sat speechless, not pretending to eat, but Mattie nibbled valiantly at her food and asked Zeena one or two questions about her visit to Bettsbridge. Zeena answered in her every-day tone and, warming to the theme, regaled them with several vivid descriptions of intestinal disturbances among her friends and relatives. She looked straight at Mattie as she spoke, a faint smile deepening the vertical lines between her nose and chin.

When supper was over she rose from her seat and pressed her hand to the flat surface over the region of her heart. "That pie of yours always sets a mite heavy, Matt," she said, not ill-naturedly. She seldom abbreviated the girl's name, and when she did so it was always a sign of affability.

"I've a good mind to go and hunt up those stomach powders I got last year over in Springfield," she continued. "I ain't tried them for quite a while, and maybe they'll help the heart-burn."

Mattie lifted her eyes. "Can't I get them for you, Zeena?" she ventured.

"No. They're in a place you don't know about." Zeena answered darkly, with one of her secret looks.

She went out of the kitchen and Mattie, [**333/334**] rising, began to clear the dishes from the table. As she passed Ethan's chair their eyes met and clung together desolately. The warm still kitchen looked as peaceful as the night before. The cat had sprung to Zeena's rocking-chair, and the heat of the fire was beginning to draw out the faint sharp scent of the geraniums. Ethan dragged himself wearily to his feet.

"I'll go out and take a look round," he said, going toward the passage to get his lantern.

As he reached the door he met Zeena coming back into the room, her lips twitching with anger, a flush of excitement on her sallow face. The shawl had slipped from her shoulders and was dragging at her down-trodden heels, and in her hands she carried the fragments of the red glass pickle-dish.

"I'd like to know who done this," she said, looking sternly from Ethan to Mattie.

There was no answer, and she continued in a trembling voice: "I went to get those powders I'd put away in father's old spectacle-case, top of the china-closet, where I keep the things I set store by, so's folks sha'n't meddle with them——" Her voice broke, and two small tears hung on her lashless lids and ran slowly down her cheeks. "It takes the step-ladder to get at the top shelf, and I put Aunt Philura Maple's pickle-dish up there o' purpose when we was married, and it's never been down since, 'cept for the spring cleaning, and then I always lifted it with my own hands, so's it shouldn't get broke." She laid the fragments reverently on the table. "I want to know who done this," she quavered.

At the challenge Ethan turned back into the room and faced her. "I can tell you, then. The cat done it."

"The *cat?*"

"That's what I said."

She looked at him hard, and then turned her eyes to Mattie, who was carrying the dish-pan to the table.

"I'd like to know how the cat got into my china-closet," she said.

"Chasin' mice, I guess," Ethan rejoined. "There was a mouse round the kitchen all last evening."

Zeena continued to look from one to the other; then she emitted her small strange laugh. "I knew the cat was a smart cat," she said in a high voice, "but I didn't know he was smart enough to pick up the pieces of my pickle-dish and lay 'em edge to edge on the very shelf he knocked 'em off of."

Mattie suddenly drew her arms out of the steaming water. "It wasn't Ethan's fault, Zeena! The cat *did* break the dish; but I got it down from the china-closet, and I'm the one to blame for its getting broken."

Zeena stood beside the ruin of her treasure, stiffening into a stony image of resentment. "*You* got down my pickle-dish—what for?"

A bright flush flew to Mattie's cheeks. "I wanted to make the supper-table pretty," she said.

"You wanted to make the supper-table pretty; and you waited till my back was turned, and took the thing I set most store by of anything I've got, and wouldn't never use it, not even when the minister come to dinner, or Aunt Martha Pierce come over from Bettsbridge—" Zeena paused with a gasp, as if terrified by her own evocation of the sacrilege. "You're a bad girl, Mattie Silver, and I always known it. It's the way your father

begun, and I was warned of it when I took you, and I tried to keep my things where you couldn't get at 'em—and now you've took from me the one I cared about most of all—" She broke off in a short spasm of sobs that passed and left her more than ever like a shape of stone.

"If I'd 'a' listened to folks, you'd 'a' gone before now, and this wouldn't 'a' happened," she said; and gathering up the bits of broken glass she went out of the room as if she carried a dead body. . . **[334/431]**

VIII

When Ethan was called back to the farm from Worcester his mother gave him, for his own use, a small room behind the untenanted "best parlour." Here he had nailed up shelves for his books, built himself a box-sofa out of boards and a mattress, laid out his papers on a kitchen-table, hung over it, on the bare wall, an engraving of Abraham Lincoln and a calendar with "Thoughts from the Poets," and tried, with these meagre materials, to produce some likeness to the study of a "minister" who had been kind to him and lent him books when he was at Worcester. He still took refuge there in summer, but when Mattie came to live with them he had had to give her his stove, and consequently the room was uninhabitable for several months of the year.

To this retreat he descended as soon as the house had grown quiet, and Zeena's steady breathing from the bed had assured him that there was to be no sequel to the scene in the kitchen. After Zeena's departure he and Mattie had stood speechless, neither seeking to approach the other. Then the girl had resumed her task of clearing up the kitchen for the night and he had taken his lantern and gone on his usual round outside the house. The kitchen was empty when he came back to it; but his tobacco-pouch and pipe had been laid on the table, and under them was a scrap of paper torn from the back of a seedsman's catalogue, on which three words were written: "Don't trouble, Ethan."

Going into his cold dark "study" he placed the lantern on the table and, stooping to its light, read the message again and again. It was the first time that Mattie had ever written to him, and the possession of the paper gave him a strange new sense of her nearness; yet it deepened his anguish by reminding him that henceforth they would have no other way of communicating with each other. For the life of her smile, the warmth of her voice, only cold paper and dead words!

Confused impulses of rebellion stormed in him. He was too young, too strong, too full of the sap of living, to submit so easily to the destruction of his hopes. Must he wear out all his years at the side of a bitter querulous woman? Other possibilities had been in him, possibilities sacrificed, one by one, to Zeena's narrow-mindedness and ignorance. And what good had come of it? She was a hundred times bitterer and more discontented than when he had married her: the one pleasure left her was to inflict pain on him. All the healthy instincts of self-defence rose up in him against such waste . . .

He bundled himself into his old coon-skin coat and lay down on the box-sofa to think. Under his cheek he felt a hard object with strange protuberances. It was a cushion which Zeena had made for him when they were engaged—the only piece of needlework he had ever seen her do. He flung it across the floor and propped his head against the wall . . .

He knew a case of a man over the mountain—a young fellow of about his own age—who had escaped from just such a life of misery by going West with the girl he cared for. His wife had divorced him, and he had married the girl and prospered. Ethan had seen the couple the summer before at Shadd's Falls, where they had come to visit relatives. They had a little girl with fair curls, who wore a gold locket and was dressed like a princess. The deserted wife had not done badly either. Her husband had given her the farm and she had managed to sell it, and with that and the alimony she had started a lunch-room at Bettsbridge and bloomed into activity and importance. Ethan was fired by the thought. Why should he not leave with Mattie the next day, instead of letting her go alone? He would hide his valise under the seat of the sleigh, and Zeena would suspect nothing till she went upstairs [**431/432**] for her nap and found a letter on the bed . . .

His impulses were still near the surface, and he sprang up, re-lit the lantern, and sat down at the table. He rummaged in the drawer for a sheet of paper, found one, and began to write.

"Zeena, I've done all I could for you, and I don't see as it's been any use. I don't blame you, nor I don't blame myself. Maybe both of us will do better separate. I'm going to try my luck West, and you can sell the farm and mill, and keep the money——"

His pen paused on the word, which brought home to him the relentless conditions of his lot. If he gave the farm and mill to Zeena, what would be left him to start his own life with? Once in the West he was sure of picking up work—he would not have feared to try his chance alone. But with Mattie depending on him the case was different. And what of Zeena's fate? Farm and mill were mortgaged to the limit of their value, and even if she found a purchaser—in itself an unlikely chance—it was doubtful if she could clear a thousand dollars on the sale. Meanwhile, how could she keep the farm going? It was only by incessant labour and personal supervision that Ethan drew a meagre living from his land, and his wife, even if she were in better health than she imagined, could never carry such a burden alone.

Well, she could go back to her people, then, and see what they would do for her. It was the fate she was forcing on Mattie—why not let her try it herself? By the time she had found out his whereabouts, and brought suit for divorce, he would probably—wherever he was—be earning enough to pay her a sufficient alimony. And the alternative was to let Mattie go forth alone, with far less hope of ultimate provision . . .

He had scattered the contents of the table-drawer in his search for a sheet of paper, and as he took up his pen his eye fell on an old copy of the *Bettsbridge Eagle*. The advertising sheet was folded uppermost, and he read the seductive words: "Trips to the West: Reduced Rates."

He drew the lantern nearer and eagerly scanned the fares; then the paper fell from his hand and he pushed aside his unfinished letter. A moment ago he had wondered what he and Mattie were to live on when they reached the West; now he saw that he had not even the money to take her there. Borrowing was out of the question: six months before he had given his only security to raise funds for necessary repairs to the mill, and he knew that without security no one at Starkfield would lend him ten dollars. The inexorable facts closed in on him like prison-warders hand-cuffing a convict. There was no way out—none. He was a prisoner for life, and now his one ray of light was to be extinguished.

He crept back wearily to the sofa, stretching himself out with limbs so heavy that he felt as if they would never move again. Tears rose in his throat and slowly burned their way to his lids.

As he lay there, the window-pane that faced him grew gradually lighter, inlaying upon the darkness a square of moon-suffused sky. A crooked tree-branch crossed it, a branch of the apple-tree under which, on summer evenings, he had sometimes found Mattie sitting when he came up from the mill. Slowly the rim of the rainy vapours caught fire and burnt away, and a pure moon swung into the blue. Ethan, rising on his elbow, watched the landscape whiten and shape itself under the sculpture of the moon. This was the night on which he was to have taken Mattie coasting, and there hung the lamp to light them! He looked out at the slopes bathed in lustre, the silver-edged darkness of the woods, the spectral purple of the hills against the sky, and it seemed as though all the beauty of the night had been poured out to mock his wretchedness . . .

He fell asleep, and when he woke the chill of the winter dawn was in the room. He felt cold and stiff and hungry, and ashamed of being hungry. He rubbed his eyes and went to the window. A red sun stood above the gray rim of the fields, behind trees that looked black and brittle. He said to himself: "This is Matt's last day," and tried to think what the place would be without her.

As he stood there he heard a step behind him and she entered.

"Oh, Ethan—were you here all night?"

She looked so small and pinched, in her poor dress, with the red scarf wound about her, and the cold light turning her paleness sallow, that Ethan stood before her without speaking. [**432/433**]

"You must be frozen," she went on, fixing lustreless eyes on him.

He drew a step nearer. "How did you know I was here?"

"Because I heard you go down stairs again after I went to bed, and I listened all night, and you didn't come up."

All his tenderness rushed to his lips. He looked at her and said: "I'll come right along and make up the kitchen fire."

They went back to the kitchen, and he fetched the coal and kindlings and cleared out the stove for her, while she brought in the milk and the cold remains of the meat-pie. When warmth began to radiate from the stove, and the first ray of sunlight lay on the kitchen floor, Ethan's dark thoughts melted in the mellower air. The sight of Mattie going about her work as he had seen her on so many mornings made it seem impossible that she should ever cease to be a part of the scene. He said to himself that he had doubtless exaggerated the significance of Zeena's threats, and that she too, with the return of daylight, would come to a saner mood.

He went up to Mattie as she bent above the stove, and laid his hand on her arm. "I don't want you should trouble either," he said, looking into her eyes with a smile.

She flushed up warmly and whispered back: "No, Ethan, I ain't going to trouble."

"I guess things'll straighten out," he added.

There was no answer but a quick throb of her lids, and he went on: "She ain't said anything this morning?"

"No. I haven't seen her yet."

"Don't you take any notice when you do."

With this injunction he left her and went out to the cow-barn. He saw Jotham Powell walking up the hill through the morning mist, and the familiar sight added to his growing conviction of security.

As the two men were clearing out the stalls Jotham rested on his pitch-fork to say: "Dan'l Byrne's goin' over to the Flats to-day noon, an' he c'd take Mattie's trunk along, and make it easier ridin' when I take her over in the sleigh."

Ethan looked at him blankly, and he continued: "Mis' Frome said the new girl'd be at the Flats at five, and I was to take Mattie then, so's 't she could ketch the six o'clock train for Stamford."

Ethan felt the blood drumming in his temples. He had to wait a moment before he could find voice to say: "Oh, it ain't so sure about Mattie's going——"

"That so?" said Jotham indifferently; and they went on with their work.

When they returned to the kitchen the two women were already at breakfast. Zeena had an air of unusual alertness and activity. She drank two cups of coffee and fed the cat with the scraps left in the

pie-dish; then she rose from her seat and, walking over to the window, snipped two or three yellow leaves from the geraniums. "Aunt Martha's ain't got a faded leaf on 'em; but they pine away when they ain't cared for," she said reflectively. Then she turned to Jotham and asked: "What time'd you say Dan'l Byrne'd be along?"

The hired man threw a hesitating glance at Ethan. "Round about noon," he said.

Zeena turned to Mattie. "That trunk of yours is too heavy for the sleigh, and Dan'l Byrne'll be round to take it over to the Flats," she said.

"I'm much obliged to you, Zeena," said Mattie.

"I'd like to go over things with you first," Zeena continued in an unperturbed voice. "I know there's a huckabuck towel missing; and I can't make out what you done with that match-safe 't used to stand behind the stuffed owl in the parlor."

She went out, followed by Mattie, and when the men were alone Jotham said to his employer: "I guess I better let Dan'l come round, then."

Ethan finished his usual morning tasks about the house and barn; then he said to Jotham: "I'm going down to Starkfield. Tell them not to wait dinner."

The passion of rebellion had broken out in him again. That which had seemed incredible in the sober light of day had really come to pass, and he was to assist as a helpless spectator at Mattie's banishment. His manhood was humbled by the part he was compelled to play and by the thought of what Mattie must think of him. Confused impulses struggled in him as he strode along to the village. He had made up his mind to do something, but he did not know what it would be.

The early mist had vanished and the fields lay like a silver shield under the sun. [**433/434**] It was one of the days when the glitter of winter shines through a pale haze of spring. Every yard of the road was alive with Mattie's presence, and there was hardly a branch against the sky or a tangle of brambles on the bank in which some bright shred of memory was not caught. Once, in the stillness, the call of a bird in a mountain ash was so like her laughter that his heart tightened and then grew large; and all these things made him see that something must be done at once.

Suddenly it occurred to him that Andrew Hale, who was a kind-hearted man, might be induced to reconsider his refusal and advance a small sum on the lumber, if he were told that Zeena's ill-health made it necessary to hire a servant. Hale, after all, knew enough of Ethan's situation to make it possible for the latter to renew his appeal without too much loss of pride; and, moreover, how much did pride count in the ebullition of passions in his breast?

The more he considered his plan the more hopeful it seemed. If he could get Mrs. Hale's ear he felt certain of success, and with fifty dollars in his pocket nothing could keep him from Mattie . . .

His first object was to reach Starkfield before Hale had started for his work; he knew the carpenter had a job down the Corbury road and was likely to leave his house early. Ethan's long strides grew more rapid with the accelerated beat of his thoughts, and as he reached the foot of School House Hill he caught sight of Hale's sleigh in the distance. He hurried forward to meet it, but as it drew nearer he saw that it was driven by the carpenter's youngest boy and that the figure at his side, looking like a large upright cocoon in spectacles, was that of Mrs. Hale. Ethan signed to them to stop, and Mrs. Hale leaned forward, her pink wrinkles twinkling with benevolence.

"Mr. Hale? Why, yes, you'll find him down home now. He ain't going to his work this forenoon. He woke up with a touch o' lumbago, and I just made him put on one of old Dr. Kidder's plasters and set right up into the fire."

Beaming maternally on Ethan, she bent over to add: "I on'y just heard from Mr. Hale 'bout Zeena's going over to Bettsbridge to see that new doctor. I'm real sorry she's feeling so bad again! I hope he thinks he can do something for her? I don't know anybody round here's had more sickness than Zeena. I always tell Mr. Hale I don't know what she'd 'a' done if she hadn't 'a' had you to look after her; and I used to say the same thing 'bout your mother. You've had an awful mean time, Ethan Frome."

She gave him a last nod of sympathy while her son chirped to the horse; and Ethan, as she drove off, stood in the middle of the road and stared after the retreating sleigh.

It was a long time since any one had spoken to him as kindly as Mrs. Hale. Most people were either indifferent to his troubles, or disposed to think it natural that a young fellow of his age should have carried without repining the burden of three crippled lives. But Mrs. Hale had said "You've had an awful mean time, Ethan Frome," and he felt less alone with his misery. If the Hales were sorry for him they would surely respond to his appeal . . .

He started down the road toward their house, but at the end of a few yards he pulled up sharply, the blood in his face. For the first time, in the light of the words he had just heard, he saw what he was about to do. He was planning to take advantage of the Hales' sympathy to obtain money from them on false pretences. That was a plain statement of the cloudy purpose which had driven him in headlong to Starkfield.

With the sudden perception of the point to which his madness had carried him, the madness fell and he saw his life before him as it was. He was a poor man, the husband of a sickly woman, whom his desertion would leave alone and destitute; and even if he had had the heart to desert her he could have done so only by deceiving two kindly people who had pitied him.

He turned and walked slowly back to the farm.

IX

At the kitchen door Daniel Byrne sat in his sleigh behind a big-boned gray who pawed the snow and swung his long head restlessly from side to side.

Ethan went into the kitchen and found his wife by the stove. Her head was [434/ 435] wrapped in her shawl, and she was reading a book called "Kidney Troubles and Their Cure" on which he had had to pay extra postage only a few days before.

Zeena did not move or look up when he entered, and after a moment he asked: "Where's Mattie?"

Without lifting her eyes from the page she replied: "I presume she's getting down her trunk."

The blood rushed to his face. "Getting down her trunk—alone?"

"Jotham Powell's down in the wood-lot, and Dan'l Byrne says he darsn't leave that horse," she returned.

Her husband, without stopping to hear the end of the phrase, had left the kitchen and sprung up the stairs. The door of Mattie's room was shut, and he wavered a moment on the landing. "Matt," he said in a low voice; but there was no answer, and he put his hand on the door-knob.

He had never been in Mattie's room except once, in the early summer, when he had gone there to plaster up a leak in the eaves, but he remembered exactly how everything had looked: the red and white quilt on her narrow bed, the pretty pin-cushion on the chest of drawers, and over it the enlarged photograph of her mother, in an oxydized frame, with a bunch of dyed grasses at the back. Now these and all other tokens of her presence had vanished, and the room looked as bare and comfortless as when Zeena had shown her into it on the day of her arrival. In the middle of the floor stood her trunk, and on the trunk she sat in her Sunday dress, her back turned to the door and her face in her hands. She had

not heard Ethan's call because she was sobbing; and she did not hear his step till he stood close behind her and laid his hands on her shoulders.

"Matt—oh, don't—oh, *Matt!*"

She started up, lifting her wet face to his. "Ethan—I thought I wasn't ever going to see you again!"

He took her in his arms, pressing her close, and with a trembling hand smoothed away the hair from her forehead.

"Not see me again? What do you mean?"

She sobbed out: "Jotham said you told him we wasn't to wait dinner for you, and I thought——"

"You thought I meant to cut it?" he finished for her grimly.

She clung to him without answering, and he laid his lips on her hair, which was soft and yet springy, like certain mosses on warm slopes, with the faint woody scent of fresh sawdust in the sun.

Through the door they heard Zeena's voice calling out from below: "Dan'l Byrne says you better hurry up if you want him to take that trunk."

They drew apart with stricken faces. Words of resistance rushed to Ethan's lips and died there. Mattie found her handkerchief and dried her eyes; then, bending down, she took hold of a handle of the trunk.

Ethan put her aside. "You let go, Matt," he ordered her.

She answered: "It takes two to coax it round the corner;" and submitting to this argument he grasped the other handle, and together they manœuvred the heavy trunk out to the landing.

"Now let go," he repeated; then he shouldered the trunk and carried it down the stairs and across the passage to the kitchen. Zeena, who had gone back to her seat by the stove, did not lift her head from her book as he passed. Mattie followed him out of the door and helped him to lift the trunk into the back of the sleigh. When it was in place they stood side by side on the door-step, watching

Daniel Byrne plunge off behind his fidgety horse.

It seemed to Ethan that his heart was bound with cords which an unseen hand was tightening with every tick of the clock. Twice he opened his lips to speak to Mattie and found no breath. At length, as she turned to re-enter the house, he laid a detaining hand on her. "I'm going to drive you over, Matt," he whispered.

She murmured back: "I think Zeena wants I should go with Jotham."

"I'm going to drive you over," he repeated; and she went into the kitchen without answering.

At dinner Ethan could not eat. If he lifted his eyes they rested on Zeena's pinched face, and the corners of her straight lips seemed to quiver away into a smile. She ate well, declaring that the mild weather made her feel better, and pressed a second helping of beans on Jotham Powell, whose wants she generally ignored.

Mattie, when the meal was over, went about her usual task of clearing the table [**435/436**] and washing up the dishes. Zeena, after feeding the cat, had returned to her rocking-chair by the stove, and Jotham Powell, who always lingered last, reluctantly pushed back his chair and moved toward the door.

On the threshold he turned back to say to Ethan: "What time'll I come round for Mattie?"

Ethan was standing near the window, mechanically filling his pipe while he watched Mattie move to and fro. He answered: "You needn't come round; I'm going to drive her over myself."

He saw the rise of the colour in Mattie's averted cheek, and the quick lifting of Zeena's head.

"I want you should stay here this afternoon, Ethan," his wife said. "Jotham can drive Mattie over."

Mattie flung an imploring glance at him, but he repeated curtly: "I'm going to drive her over myself."

Zeena continued in the same even tone: "I wanted you should stay and fix up that stove in Mattie's room afore the girl gets here. It ain't been drawing right for nigh on a month now."

Ethan's voice rose indignantly. "If it was good enough for Mattie I guess it's good enough for a hired girl."

"That girl that's coming told me she was used to a house where they had a furnace," Zeena persisted with the same monotonous mildness.

"She'd better ha' stayed there then," he flung back at her; and turning to Mattie he added in a hard voice: "You be ready by three, Matt; I've got business at Corbury."

Jotham Powell had started for the barn, and Ethan strode down after him aflame wth anger. The pulses in his temples throbbed and a fog was in his eyes. He went about his task without knowing what force directed him, or whose hands and feet were fulfilling its orders. It was not till he led out the sorrel and backed him between the shafts of the sleigh that he once more became conscious of what he was doing. As he passed the bridle over the horse's head, and wound the traces around the shafts, he remembered the day when he had made the same preparations in order to drive over and meet his wife's cousin at the Flats. It was little more than a year ago, on just such a soft afternoon, with a "feel" of spring in the air. The sorrel, turning the same big ringed eye on him, nuzzled the palm of his hand in the same way; and one by one all the days between rose up and stood before him . . .

He flung the bearskin into the sleigh, climbed to the seat, and drove up to the house. When he entered the kitchen it was empty, but Mattie's bag and shawl lay ready by the door. He went to the foot of the stairs and listened. No sound reached him from above, but presently he thought he heard some one moving about in his deserted study, and pushing open the door he saw Mattie, in her hat and jacket, standing with her back to him near the table.

She started at his approach and turning quickly, said: "Is it time?"

"What are you doing here, Matt?" he asked her.

She looked at him timidly. "I was just taking a look round—that's all," she answered, with a wavering smile.

They went back into the kitchen without speaking, and Ethan picked up her bag and shawl.

"Where's Zeena?" he asked.

"She went upstairs right after dinner. She said she had those shooting pains again, and didn't want to be disturbed."

"Didn't she say goodbye to you?"

"No. That was all she said."

Ethan, looking slowly about the kitchen, said to himself with a shudder that in a few hours he would be returning to it alone. Then the sense of unreality overcame him once more, and he could not bring himself to believe that Mattie stood there for the last time before him.

"Come on," he said almost gaily, opening the door and putting her bag into the sleigh. He sprang to his seat and bent over to tuck the rug about her as she slipped into the place at his side. "Now then, go 'long," he said, with a shake of the reins that sent the sorrel placidly jogging down the hill.

"We got lots of time for a good ride, Matt!" he cried, seeking her hand beneath the fur and pressing it in his. His face tingled and he felt dizzy, as if he had stopped in at the Starkfield saloon on a zero day for a drink.

At the gate, instead of making for Starkfield, he turned the sorrel to the right, up [**436/437**] the Bettsbridge road. Mattie sat silent, giving no sign of surprise; but after a moment she said: "Are you going round by Shadow Pond?"

He laughed and answered: "I knew you'd know!"

She drew closer under the bearskin, so that, looking sideways around his coat-sleeve, he could just catch the tip of her nose and a blown brown wave of hair. They drove slowly up the road between fields glistening under the pale sun, and then bent to the right down a lane edged with spruce and larch. Ahead of them, a long way off, a range of hills stained by patches of black forest flowed away in round white curves against the sky. The lane passed into a pine-wood with boles reddening in the afternoon sun and delicate blue shadows on the snow. As they entered it the breeze fell and a warm stillness seemed to drop from the branches with the dropping needles. Here the snow was so pure that the tiny tracks of wood-animals had left on it intricate lace-like patterns, and the bluish cones caught in its surface stood out like ornaments of bronze.

Ethan drove on in silence till they reached a part of the wood where the pines were more widely spaced; then he drew up and helped Mattie to get out of the sleigh. They passed between the aromatic trunks, the snow breaking crisply under their feet, till they came to a sheet of water with steep wooded sides. Across its frozen surface, from the farther bank, a single hill rising against the western sun threw the long, conical shadow which gave the lake its name. It was a shy secret spot, full of the same dumb melancholy that Ethan felt in his heart.

He looked up and down the little pebbly beach till his eye lit on a fallen tree-trunk half submerged in snow.

"There's where we sat at the picnic," he reminded her.

The entertainment of which he spoke was one of the few that they had taken part in together: a "church picnic" which, on a long afternoon of the preceding summer, had filled the retired place with merry-making. Mattie had begged him to go with her but he had refused. Then, toward sunset, coming down from the mountain where he had been felling timber, he had been caught by some strayed revellers and drawn into the group by the lake, where Mattie, encircled by facetious youths, and bright as a blackberry under her spreading hat, was brewing coffee over a gipsy fire. He remembered the shyness he had felt at approaching her in his uncouth clothes, and then the lighting up of her face, and the way she had broken through the group to come to him with a cup in her hand. They had sat for a few minutes on the fallen log by the pond, and she had missed her gold locket, and set the young men searching for it; and it was Ethan who had spied it in the moss . . . That was all; but all their intercourse had been made up of just such inarticulate flashes, when they seemed to come suddenly upon happiness as if they had surprised a butterfly in the winter woods . . .

"It was right there I found your locket," he said, pushing his foot into a dense tuft of blueberry bushes.

"I never saw anybody with such sharp eyes!" she answered.

She sat down on the tree-trunk in the sun and he sat down beside her.

"You were as pretty as a picture in that pink hat," he said.

She laughed with pleasure. "Oh, I guess it was the hat!" she rejoined.

They had never before avowed their inclination so openly, and Ethan, for a moment, had the illusion that he was a free man, wooing the girl he meant to marry. He looked at her hair and longed to touch it again, and to tell her that it smelt of the woods; but he never had learned to say such things.

Suddenly she rose to her feet and said: "We mustn't stay here any longer."

He continued to gaze at her vaguely, only half-roused from his dream. "There's plenty of time," he answered.

They stood looking at each other as if the eyes of each were straining to absorb and hold fast the other's image. There were things he had to say to her before they parted, but he could not say them in that place of summer memories, and he turned and followed her in silence to the sleigh. As they drove away the sun sank behind the hill and the pine-boles turned from red to gray.

By a devious track between the fields they wound back to the Starkfield road. Under the open sky the light was still clear, [437/438] with a reflection of cold red on the eastern hills. The clumps of trees in the snow seemed to draw together in ruffled lumps, like birds with their heads under their wings; and the sky, as it paled, rose higher, leaving the earth more alone.

As they turned into the Starkfield road Ethan said: "Matt, what do you mean to do?"

She did not answer at once, but at length she said: "I'll try to get a place in a store."

"You know you can't do it. The bad air and the standing all day nearly killed you before."

"I'm a lot stronger than I was before I came to Starkfield."

"And now you're going to throw away all the good it's done you!"

There seemed to be no answer to this, and again they drove on for a while without speaking. With every yard of the way some spot where they had stood, and laughed together or been silent, clutched at Ethan and dragged him back.

"Isn't there any of your father's folks could help you?"

"There isn't any of 'em I'd ask."

He lowered his voice to say: "You know there's nothing I wouldn't do for you if I could."

"I know there isn't."

"But I can't——"

She was silent, but he felt a slight tremor in the shoulder against his.

"Oh, Matt," he broke out, "if I could ha' gone with you now I'd ha' done it——"

She turned to him, pulling a scrap of paper from her breast. "Ethan—I found this," she stammered. Even in the failing light he saw it was the letter to his wife that he had begun the night before and forgotten to destroy. Through his astonishment there ran a fierce thrill of joy. "Matt"—he cried; "if I could ha' done it, would you?"

"Oh, Ethan, Ethan—what's the use?" With a sudden movement she tore the letter in shreds and let them flutter off into the snow.

"Tell me, Matt! Tell me!" he adjured her.

She was silent for a moment; then she said, in such a low tone that he had to stoop his head to hear her: "I used to think of it sometimes, summer nights, when the moon was so bright I couldn't sleep."

His heart reeled with the sweetness of it. "As long ago as that?"

She answered, as if the date had long been fixed for her: "The first time was at Shadow Pond."

"Was that why you gave me my coffee before the others?"

"I don't know. Did I? I was dreadfully put out when you wouldn't go to the picnic with me; and then, when I saw you coming down the road, I thought maybe you'd gone home that way o' purpose; and that made me glad."

They were silent again. They had reached the point where the road dipped to the hollow by Ethan's mill and as they descended the darkness descended with them, dropping down like a black veil from the hemlock boughs.

"I'm tied hand and foot, Matt. There isn't a thing I can do," he began again.

"You must write to me sometimes, Ethan."

"Oh, what good'll writing do? I want to put my hand out and touch you. I want to do for you and care for you. I want to be there when you're sick and when you're lonesome."

"You mustn't think but what I'll do all right."

"You won't need me, you mean? I suppose you'll marry!"

"Oh, Ethan!" she cried.

"I don't know how it is you make me feel, Matt. I'd a'most rather have you dead than that."

"Oh, I wish I was, I wish I was!" she sobbed.

The sound of her weeping shook him out of his dark rage, and he felt ashamed.

"Don't let's talk that way," he whispered.

"Why shouldn't we, when it's true? I've been wishing it every minute of the day."

"Matt! You be quiet! Don't you say it."

"There's never anybody been good to me but you."

"Don't say that either, when I can't lift a hand for you!"

"Yes, but it's true just the same."

They had reached the top of School House Hill and saw Starkfield below them in the twilight. A cutter, mounting the road from the village, passed them by in a [438/439] joyous flutter of bells, and they straightened themselves and looked ahead with rigid faces. Along the main street lights had begun to shine from the house-fronts and stray figures were turning in here and there at the gates. Ethan, with a touch of his whip, roused the sorrel to a languid trot.

As they drew near the end of the village the cries of children reached them, and they saw a knot of boys, with sleds behind them, scattering across the open space before the church.

"I guess this'll be their last coast for a day or two," Ethan said, looking up at the mild sky.

Mattie was silent, and he added: "We were to have gone down last night."

Still she did not speak and, prompted by an obscure desire to help himself and her through their miserable last hour, he went on discursively: "Ain't it funny we haven't been down together but just that once last winter?"

She answered: "It wasn't often I got down to the village."

"That's so," he said.

They had reached the crest of the Corbury road, and between the indistinct white glimmer of the church and the black curtain of the Varnum spruces the slope stretched away below them without a sled on its length. Some erratic impulse prompted Ethan to say: "How'd you like me to take you down now."

She forced a laugh. "Why, there isn't time!"

"There's all the time we want. Come along!" His one desire now was to postpone the moment of turning the sorrel toward the Flats.

"But the girl," she faltered. "She'll be waiting at the station."

"Well, let her wait. You'd have to if she didn't. Come!"

The authority in his voice seemed to subdue her, and when he had jumped from the sleigh she let him help her out, saying only, with a vague feint of reluctance: "But there isn't a sled round anywheres."

"Yes, there is! Right over there under the spruces."

He threw the bearskin over the sorrel, who stood passively by the roadside, hanging a meditative head. Then he caught Mattie's hand and drew her after him toward the sled.

She seated herself and he took his place behind her, so close that her hair brushed his face. "All right, Matt?" he called out, as if the width of the road had been between them.

She turned her head to say: "It's dreadfully dark. Are you sure you can see?"

He laughed contemptuously: "I could go down this coast with my eyes tied!" and she laughed with him, as if she liked his audacity. Nevertheless he sat still a moment, straining his eyes down the long hill, for it was the most confusing hour of the evening, the hour when the last clearness from the upper sky is merged with the rising night in a blur that disguises landmarks and falsifies distances.

"Now!" he cried.

The sled started with a bound, and they flew on through the dusk, gathering smoothness and speed as they went, with the hollow night opening out below them and the air singing by like an organ. Mattie sat perfectly still, but as they

reached the bend at the foot of the hill, where the big elm thrust out a dangerous elbow, he fancied that she shrank a little closer.

"Don't be scared, Matt!" he cried exultantly, as they spun safely past it and flew down the second slope; and when they reached the level ground beyond, and the speed of the sled began to slacken, he heard her give a little laugh of glee.

They sprang off and started to walk back up the hill. Ethan dragged the sled with one hand and passed the other through Mattie's arm.

"Were you scared I'd run you into the elm?" he asked with a boyish laugh.

"I told you I was never scared with you," she answered.

The strange exaltation of his mood had brought on one of his rare fits of boastfulness. "It *is* a tricky place, though. The least swerve, and we'd never ha' come up again. But I can measure distances to a hair's-breadth—always could."

She murmured: "I always say you've got the surest eye . . ."

Deep silence had fallen with the starless dusk, and they leaned on each other without speaking; but at every step of their climb Ethan said to himself: "It's the last time we'll ever walk together."

They mounted slowly to the top of the hill. When they were abreast of the [439/440] church he stooped his head to her to ask: "Are you tired?" and she answered, breathing quickly: "It was splendid!"

With a pressure of his arm he guided her toward the Norway spruces. "I guess this sled must be Ned Hale's. Anyhow I'll leave it where I found it." He drew the sled up to the Varnum gate and rested it against the fence. As he raised himself he felt Mattie close to him among the shadows.

"Is this where Ned and Ruth kissed each other?" she whispered breathlessly, and flung her arms about him. Her lips, groping for his, swept over his face, and he held her fast in a rapture of surprise.

"Good-bye—good-bye," she stammered, and kissed him again.

"Oh, Matt, I can't let you go!" broke from him in the same old cry.

She freed herself from his hold and he heard her sobbing. "Oh, I can't go either!" she wailed.

"Matt! What'll we do? What'll we do?"

They clung to each other's hands like children, and her body shook with desperate sobs.

Through the stillness they heard the church clock striking five.

"Oh, Ethan, it's time!" she cried.

He drew her back to him. "Time for what? You don't suppose I'm going to leave you?"

"If I missed my train where'd I go?"

"Where are you going if you catch it?"

She stood silent, her hands lying cold and relaxed in his.

"What's the good of either of us going anywheres without the other one now?" he said.

She remained motionless, as if she had not heard him. Then she snatched her hands from his, threw her arms about his neck, and pressed her wet cheek to his face. "Ethan! Ethan! I want you to take me down again!"

"Down where?"

"The coast. Right off. So 't we'll never come up any more."

"Matt! What on earth do you mean?"

She put her lips close against his ear to say: "Right into the big elm. You said you could. So 't we'd never have to leave each other any more."

"Why, what are you talking of? You're crazy!"

"I'm not crazy; but I will be if I leave you."

"Oh, Matt, Matt—" he groaned.

She tightened her fierce hold about his neck. "Ethan, where'll I go if I leave you? I don't know how to get along alone. You said so yourself just now. Nobody but you was ever good to me. And there'll be that strange girl in the house . . . and she'll sleep in my bed, where I used to lay nights and listen to hear you come upstairs. . ."

The words were like fragments torn from his heart. With them came the hated vision of the house he was going back to—of the stairs he would have to go up every night, of the woman who would wait for him there. And the sweetness of Mattie's avowal, the wild wonder of knowing at last that all that had happened to him had happened to her too, made the other vision more abhorrent, the other life more intolerable to return to . . .

Her pleadings still came to him between short sobs, but he no longer heard what she was saying. Her hat had slipped back, and he was stroking her hair. He wanted to get the feeling of it into his hand, so that it would sleep there like a seed in winter. Once he found her mouth again, and they seemed to be by the pond together in the burning August sun. But his cheek touched hers, and it was cold and full of weeping, and he saw the road to the Flats under the night and heard the whistle of the train up the line.

The black trees swathed them in night and silence. They might have been in their coffins underground. He said to himself: "Perhaps it'll feel like this . . ." and then again: "After this I sha'n't feel anything. . ." Suddenly he heard the old sorrel whinny across the road, and thought: "He's wondering why he doesn't get his supper. . ."

"Come," Mattie whispered, tugging at his hand.

Her sombre violence constrained him: she seemed the embodied instrument of fate. He pulled the sled out, blinking like a night-bird as he passed from the shade of the spruces into the relative clearness of the open. The slope below them was deserted. All Starkfield was at supper, and not a figure crossed the open space before the church. The sky, swollen with the clouds [**440/441**] that announce a thaw, hung as low as before a summer storm. He strained his eyes through the dimness, and they seemed less keen, less capable than usual.

He took his seat on the sled and Mattie

instantly placed herself in front of him. Her hat had fallen into the snow and his lips were in her hair. He stretched out his legs, drove his heels into the road to keep the sled from slipping forward, and bent her head back between his hands. Then suddenly he sprang up again.

"Get up," he ordered her.

It was the tone she always heeded, but she cowered down in her seat, repeating vehemently: "No, no, no!"

"Get up!"

"Why?"

"I want to sit in front."

"No, no! How can you steer in front?"

"I don't have to. We'll follow the track."

They spoke in smothered whispers, as though the night were listening.

"Get up! Get up!" he urged her; but she kept on repeating: "Why do you want to sit in front?"

"Because I—because I want to feel you holding me," he stammered, and dragged her to her feet.

The answer seemed to satisfy her, or else she yielded to the power of his voice. He bent down, feeling in the obscurity for the glassy slide worn by preceding coasters, and placed the runners carefully between its edges. She waited while he seated himself with crossed legs in the front of the sled; then she crouched quickly down at his back and clasped her arms about him. Her breath in his neck set him shuddering again, and he almost sprang from his seat. But in a flash he remembered the alternative. She was right: this was better than parting. He leaned back and drew her mouth to his. . .

Just as they started he heard the sorrel's whinny again, and the familiar wistful call, and all the confused images it brought with it, went with him down the first reach of the road. Half-way down there was a sudden drop, then a rise, and after that another long delirious descent. As they took wing for this it seemed to him that they were flying indeed, flying far up into the cloudy night, with Starkfield immeasurably below them, falling away like a speck in space. . . Then the big elm shot up ahead, lying in wait for them at the bend of the road, and he said between his teeth: "We can fetch it; I know we can fetch it——"

As they flew toward the tree Mattie pressed her arms tighter, and her blood seemed to be in his veins. Once or twice the sled swerved a little under them. He slanted his body to keep it headed for the elm, repeating to himself again and again: "I know we can fetch it"; and little phrases she had spoken ran through his head and danced before him on the air. The big tree loomed bigger and closer, and as they bore down on it he thought: "It's waiting for us: it seems to know." But suddenly his wife's face, with twisted monstrous lineaments, thrust itself between him and his goal, and he made an instinctive movement to brush it aside. The sled swerved in response, but he righted it again, kept it straight, and drove down on the black projecting mass. There was a last instant when the air shot past him like millions of fiery wires; and then the elm . . .

The sky was still thick, but looking straight up he saw a single star, and tried vaguely to reckon whether it were Sirius, or—or— The effort tired him too much, and he closed his heavy lids and thought that he would sleep. . . The stillness was so profound that he heard a little animal twittering somewhere near by under the snow. It made a small frightened *cheep* like a fieldmouse, and he wondered languidly if it were hurt. Then he understood that it must be in pain: pain so excruciating that he seemed, mysteriously, to feel it shooting through his own body. He tried in vain to roll over in the direction of the sound, and stretched his left arm out across the snow. And now it was as though he felt rather than heard the twittering; it seemed to be under his palm, which rested on something soft and springy. The thought of the animal's suffering was intolerable to him, and he struggled to raise himself, and could not, because a rock, or some huge mass, seemed to be lying on him. But he continued to finger about cautiously with his left hand, thinking he might get hold of the little creature and help it; and all at once he knew that the soft thing he had touched was Mattie's hair and that his hand was on her face. [**441/442**]

He dragged himself to his knees, the monstrous load on him moving with him as he moved, and his hand went over and over her face, and he felt that the twittering came from her lips . . .

He got his face down close to hers, with his ear to her mouth, and in the darkness he saw her eyes open and heard her say his name.

"Oh, Matt, I thought we'd fetched it," he moaned; and far off, up the hill, he heard the sorrel whinny, and thought: "I ought to be getting him his feed. . ."

. . . .

. . . .

The querulous drone ceased as I entered Frome's kitchen, and of the two women sitting there I could not tell which had been the speaker.

One of them, on my appearing, raised her tall bony figure from her seat, not as if to welcome me—for she threw me no more than a brief glance of surprise—but simply to set about preparing the meal which Frome's absence had delayed. A slatternly calico wrapper hung from her shoulders and the wisps of her thin gray hair were drawn away from a high forehead and fastened at the back by a broken comb. She had pale opaque eyes which revealed nothing and reflected nothing, and her narrow lips were of the same sallow colour as her face.

The other woman was much smaller and slighter. She sat huddled in an armchair near the stove, and when I came in she turned her head quickly toward me, without the least corresponding movement of her body. Her hair was as gray as her companion's, her face as bloodless and shrivelled, but amber-tinted, with swarthy shadows sharpening the nose and

hollowing the temples. Under her shapeless dress her body kept its limp immobility, and her dark eyes had the bright witch-like stare that disease of the spine often gives.

Even for that part of the country the kitchen was a poor-looking place. With the exception of the dark-eyed woman's chair, which looked like a soiled relic of luxury bought at a country auction, the furniture was of the roughest kind. Three coarse china plates and a broken-nosed milk-jug had been set on a greasy table scored with knife-cuts, and a couple of straw-bottomed chairs and a kitchen dresser of unpainted pine stood out meagrely against the plaster walls.

"My, it's cold here! The fire must be 'most out," Frome said, glancing about him apologetically as he followed me in.

The tall woman, who had moved away from us toward the dresser, took no notice; but the other, from her cushioned niche, answered complainingly, in a high thin voice: "It's on'y just been made up this very minute. Zeena fell asleep and slep' ever so long, and I thought I'd be frozen stiff before I could wake her up and get her to 'tend to it."

I knew then that it was she who had been speaking when we entered.

Her companion, who was just coming back to the table with the remains of a cold mince-pie in a battered pie-dish, set down her unappetizing burden without appearing to hear the accusation brought against her.

Frome stood hesitatingly before her as she advanced; then he looked at me and said: "This is my wife, Mis' Frome." After another interval he added, turning toward the figure in the arm-chair: "And this is Miss Mattie Silver. . ."

. . . .

Mrs. Hale, tender soul, had pictured me as lost in the Flats and buried under a snow-drift; and so lively was her satisfaction on seeing me safely restored to her the next morning, that I felt my peril had caused me to advance several degrees in her favour.

Great was her amazement, and that of old Mrs. Varnum, on learning that Ethan Frome's old horse had carried me to and from Corbury Junction through the worst blizzard of the winter; greater still their surprise when they heard that his master had taken me in for the night.

Beneath their wondering exclamations I felt a secret curiosity to know what impressions I had received from my night in the Frome household, and divined that the best way of breaking down their reserve was to let them try to penetrate mine. I therefore confined myself to saying, in a matter-of-fact tone, that I had been received with great kindness, and that Frome had made a bed for me in a room on the ground floor which seemed in happier days [**442/443**] to have been fitted up as a kind of writing-room or study.

"Well," Mrs. Hale mused, "in such a storm I suppose he felt he couldn't do less than take you in—but I guess it went hard with Ethan. I don't believe but what you're the only stranger has set foot in that house for over twenty years. He's that proud he don't even like his oldest friends to go there; and I don't know as any do, any more, except myself and the doctor. . ."

"You still go there, Mrs. Hale?" I ventured.

"I used to go a good deal after the accident, when I was first married; but after a while I got to think it made 'em feel worse to see us. And then one thing and another came, and my own troubles . . . But I generally make out to drive over there round about New Year's, and once in the summer. Only I always try to pick a day when Ethan's off somewheres. It's bad enough to see the two women sitting there—but *his* face, when he looks round that bare place, just kills me . . . You see, I can look back and call it up in his mother's day, before their troubles."

Old Mrs. Varnum, by this time, had gone up to bed, and her daughter and I were sitting alone, after supper, in the austere seclusion of the horse-hair parlour. Mrs. Hale glanced at me tentatively, as though trying to see how much footing my conjectures gave her; and I guessed that if she had kept silence till now it was because she had been waiting, through all the years, for some one who should see what she alone had seen.

I waited to let her trust in me gather strength before I said: "Yes, it's pretty bad, seeing all three of them there together."

She drew her mild brows into a frown of pain. "It was just awful from the beginning. I was here in the house when they were carried up—they laid Mattie Silver in the room you're in. She and I were great friends, and she was to have been my bridesmaid that spring . . . When she came to I went up to her and stayed with her all night. They gave her things to quiet her, and she didn't know much till to'rd morning, and then all of a sudden she woke up just like herself, and looked straight at me out of her big eyes, and said . . . Oh, I don't know why I'm telling you all this," Mrs. Hale broke off, crying.

She took off her spectacles, wiped the moisture from them, and put them on again with an unsteady hand. "It got about the next day," she went on, "that Zeena Frome had sent Mattie off in a hurry because she had a hired girl coming, and the folks here could never rightly tell what she and Ethan were doing that night coasting, when they'd ought to have been on their way to the Flats to ketch the train . . . I never knew myself what Zeena thought—I don't to this day. Nobody knows Zeena's thoughts. Anyhow, when she heard o' the accident she came right in and stayed with Ethan over to the minister's, where they'd carried him. And as soon as the doctors said that Mattie could be moved, Zeena sent for her and took her back to the farm."

"And there she's been ever since?"

Mrs. Hale answered simply: "There

was nowhere else for her to go"; and my heart tightened at the thought of the hard necessities of the poor.

"Yes, there she's been," Mrs. Hale continued, "and Zeena's done for her, and done for Ethan, as good as she could. It was a miracle, considering how sick she was—but she seemed to be raised right up just when the call came to her. Not as she's ever given up doctoring, and she's had sick spells right along; but she's had the strength given her to care for those two for over twenty years, and before the accident came she thought she couldn't even care for herself."

Mrs. Hale paused a moment, and I remained silent, plunged in the vision of what her words evoked. "It's horrible for them all," I murmured.

"Yes: it's pretty bad. And they ain't any of 'em easy people either. Mattie *was,* before the accident; I never knew a sweeter nature. But she's suffered too much—that's what I always say when folks tell me how she's soured. And Zeena, she was always cranky. Not but what she bears with Mattie wonderful— I've seen that myself. But sometimes the two of them get going at each other, and then Ethan's face'd break your heart . . . When I see that, I think it's *him* that suffers most . . . anyhow it ain't Zeena, because she ain't got the time . . . It's a pity, though," Mrs. [**443**/**444**] Hale ended, sighing, "that they're all shut up there'n that one kitchen. In the summertime, on pleasant days, they move Mattie into the parlour, or out in the door-yard, and that makes it easier . . . but winters there's the fires to be thought of; and there ain't a dime to spare up at the Fromes'."

Mrs. Hale drew a deep breath, as though her memory were eased of its long burden, and she had no more to say; but suddenly an impulse of complete avowal seized her.

She took off her spectacles again, leaned toward me across the bead-work table-cover, and went on with lowered voice: "There was one day, about a week after the accident, when they all thought Mattie couldn't live. Well, I say it's a pity she did. I said it right out to our minister once, and he was shocked at me. Only he wasn't with me that morning when she first came to . . . and I say, if she'd ha' died, Ethan might ha' lived; and the way they are now, I don't see's there's much difference between the Fromes up at the farm and the Fromes down in the graveyard; 'cept that down there they're all quiet, and the women have got to hold their tongues."

PART TWO

THE GENESIS OF THE STORY

An Early Version of the "Prologue"*

EDITH WHARTON evidently worked her way slowly, in the winter of 1910–1911, toward the final version of *Ethan Frome*. The manuscript she submitted to the publishers has not been found. The two surviving sections of what would appear to be the next-to-last revision include not only grafts from earlier versions, cut from the manuscript and joined to this version, but many rejected words, phrases, and sentences, indicating a constant process of emendation. One of these sections (the other is the "Epilogue"), which constitutes the prologue to the story proper, is reproduced below in the final form that Mrs. Wharton clearly intended for this version.

I had the story, bit by bit, from various people; and, as generally happens in such cases, each time it was a different story.

If you know Starkfield, Massachusetts, you know the post-office. If you know the post-office you must have seen Ethan Frome drive up to it, drop the reins on his hollow-backed bay and drag himself across the brick pavement to the white colonnade; and you must have asked who he was.

It was there that, several years ago, I saw him for the first time; and the sight pulled me up sharp.

Even then he was easily the most striking figure in Starkfield, though he was but the ruin of a man. It was not so much his great height that marked him, for the "natives," I had already noted, were easily singled out by their lank longitude from the stockier growth of foreign breed: it was the powerful negligent way in which he carried his inches, in spite of the limp that checked each step like the jerk of a chain. There was something bleak and unapproachable in the look of his face, and he was so stiffened and grizzled that I took him for an old man, and was surprised to learn that he was barely fifty. I had this from Harmon Gow, who had driven the stage from Bettsbridge to Starkfield in pre-trolley days, and knew the chronicle of all the families on his line.

"He's looked that way ever since he had his smash-up; and that's twenty-five years ago come next February," Harmon threw out between reminiscent pauses.

The "smash-up" it was—as I gathered from the same source—which, besides drawing the deep-red gash across Ethan Frome's forehead, had so shortened and distorted his right side from shoulder to ankle that his powers of locomotion were strained by the brief hobble between his buggy and the post-office window. It was his daily habit to drive in from his farm at about midday, and as that was my own hour for fetching my mail I almost invariably passed him under the pillared porch, or stood beside him while we waited on the motions of the distributing hand behind the grating. I noticed that, though he came so punctually, he seldom received anything but a copy of the Bettsbridge Eagle, which he thrust without a glance into his sagging pocket. At intervals, however, the post-master would hand him an envelope addressed to Mrs. Zenobia—or Mrs. Zeena—Frome, and

* Edith Wharton, from the incomplete manuscript of an early version of *Ethan Frome* in the Yale Collection of American Literature. Reprinted with the permission of A. Watkins, Inc. and the Yale University Library.

usually bearing conspicuously in the upper corner the address of some manufacturer of patent medicine and the name of his specific. These documents my neighbour would also pocket without a glance, as if too much used to them to wonder at their number and variety, and would then turn away with a silent nod to the post-master. Every one in Starkfield knew him and gave him a greeting unconsciously tempered to his own sober mien; but his evident unsociability was respected, and it was only on rare occasions that one of the older men of the place detained him for a word. When this happened he would listen quietly, his blue eyes on the speaker's face, and answer in so low a tone that his words never reached me; then he would climb stiffly into his buggy, gather up in his left hand the reins in the hollow of the bay's back, and drive slowly away in the direction of his saw mill.

"It was a pretty bad smash-up?" I questioned Harmon, looking after Frome's retreating figure, and thinking how gallantly his lean brown head, with its shock of light hair, must have been set on his shoulders before they were bent out of shape.

"Wust kind," my informant assented. "More'n enough to kill most men. But the Fromes are tough. Ethan'll likely touch a hundred."

"Good God!" I exclaimed involuntarily.

At that moment, Ethan Frome, who had climbed to his seat, leaned back to assure himself of the security of a wooden box—also with a druggist's label on it—which he had placed in the back of the buggy, and I saw his face as it probably looked when he thought himself alone.

"*That* man touch a hundred? He looks as if he was dead and in hell now."

Harmon cut a piece of tobacco and pressed it into the leather pouch of his cheek.

"Guess he's been in Starkfield too many winters. Most of the smart ones get away."

"Why didn't *he?*"

Harmon considered. "Somebody had to stay and care for the women. There warn't anybody but Ethan. First his mother—then his wife."

"And then the smash-up?"

Harmon chuckled sardonically. "That's so. He *had* to stay then."

"I see. And since then they've had to care for him?"

Harmon considered. "Oh, as to that: I guess it's always Ethan that done the caring."

Harmon developed the tale as far as his mental and moral reach permitted, but there were obscure gaps between his facts, and I had the sense that the secret meaning of the story was in the gaps. One phrase stuck in my memory, and served as the nucleus about which I grouped my subsequent inferences. "Guess he's been in Starkfield too many winters."

Before my own time there was up I had learned to know what that meant. Yet I had come in the degenerate day of the trolley, bicycle, and rural delivery, when communication was easy between the scattered mountain villages, and the bigger towns, such as Bettsbridge and Shadd's Falls, had libraries, theatres, and Y.M.C.A. halls to which the youth of the hills could descend for recreation. But when winter shut down on Starkfield, and the village lay under a sheet of snow perpetually renewed from the laden skies, I began to see what life there—or rather its negation—must have been in Ethan Frome's youth.

I had been sent up by my employers on a job connected with the big power-house at Corbury Junction, and a long-drawn carpenters' strike had so delayed the work that I found myself anchored at Starkfield—the nearest habitable spot—for the best part of the winter. I chafed at first, and then, under the hypnotizing effect of routine, gradually began to find a grim fascination in the life. I was struck at first by the contrast between the vitality of the climate and the deadness of the community. Day after day, when the December snows were over, a blazing blue sky poured down torrents of light and air on the white landscape, which gave them back in a glitter of intenser whiteness. One would have supposed that such an atmosphere would have quickened the emotions as well as the blood; but it seemed to produce no change except that of retarding the sluggish pulse of Starkfield. When I had been there a little longer, and had learned that this phase of crystal clearness was only the prelude to a long period of biting sunless cold; when I had seen the storms of February pitch their white tents about the devoted village, and heard the wild cavalry of March winds charge down from the north to their support, I understood why Starkfield emerged from its six months' siege like a starved garrison capitulating without quarter. Twenty years earlier the means of resistance must have been far fewer, and the enemy in command of almost all lines of communication between the beleaguered villages; and I began to measure the retrospective significance of Harmon's phrase. But, since all the "smart ones" got out, what could have condemned a man of Ethan Frome's make to life-long imprisonment in Starkfield?

Various people gave me various reasons, and out of them I pieced together an explanation that might have sufficed if the accident of personal contact with the man had not intensified my desire to find a clue to something in his face that even the loneliness of the New England winter could not have put there. On my arrival I had arranged with Denis Eady, the grocer, (who kept the nearest approach to a livery-stable that Starkfield possessed) for the hire of a vehicle to carry me daily to Corbury Flats, where I picked up my train for the Junction. But about the middle of the winter Eady's two horses fell ill. The malady spread to the other Starkfield stables, and for a day or two I was put to it to find a means of transport. Then Harmon Eddy [sic] suggested that Ethan Frome's bay was still on his legs,

and that his owner might be willing to come to my rescue.

I stared at the suggestion. "Ethan Frome? I've never even spoken to the man. Why should he put himself out for me?"

Harmon's answer surprised me still more. "I don't know as he would; but I know he'd be glad to earn a dollar."

I had been told that Frome was poor, and that the saw-mill and the stony acres of his upland farm yielded scarcely enough to keep him and his household through the winter months; but I had not supposed him to be in such want as Harmon's words implied.

"Is he as poor as that?" I exclaimed.

"Well, things ain't gone any too well with him. When a man's been setting around like a hulk for twenty years or more, seeing things that want doing, it eats inter him, and he loses his grit. That Frome farm was always 'bout as bare's a milk-pan when the cat's been round; and you know what one er them old watermill's worth nowadays. When Ethan could sweat over 'em both from sun-up to dark he kinder choked a living out of 'em; but his folks ate up most everything, even then, and I don't see how he makes out now. His mother dragged along sick for years afore she died, and his wife Zeena's the greatest hand at doctoring in the county. Sickness and trouble: that's what Ethan's had on his plate ever since the first helping."

The next morning, when I emerged from my boarding-house, I saw the hollow-backed bay at the gate, and Ethan Frome, throwing back a worn coon-skin rug, made room for me in the sleigh at his side. After that for a week, he drove me over every morning to Corbury Flats, where I picked up a train for the Junction; and on my return, in the afternoon, he met me again and carried me back through the icy night to Starkfield. The distance each way was barely three miles, but the old bay's pace was slow, and even when there was a firm surface of snow under the runners we were nearly an hour on the way. Ethan Frome drove in silence, the reins loosely held in his left hand, his brown seamed profile under its fur cap sharply drawn against the walls of snow along the road-side. He never turned his face to mine, or answered, except in monosyllables, the questions I put, or such slight pleasantries as I ventured. Yet I had no sense of constraint with him. He seemed, somehow, a part of the mute melancholy landscape, an incarnation of its frozen woe, with all that was warm and sentient in him fast bound below the surface. But there was nothing repellent in his silence. I simply felt that he lived in a depth of moral isolation too remote for casual access; and I was drawn to him by the sense that his loneliness was not merely the result of his personal plight, tragic as I guessed that to be, but had in it the profound accumulated cold of many Starkfield winters.

Only once or twice was the distance between us bridged for a moment; and the glimpses thus gained of him confirmed my desire to know more. Once I made some allusion to an engineering job I had superintended the previous winter in Florida, and to the contrast between the scenes about us, and those in which I had found myself a year earlier; and Frome said: "Yes, I was down there once, and for a good while afterward I could call up the sight of it in winter. But now it's all snowed under."

He vouchsafed no more, and I had to let the inflection of his voice, and his abrupt relapse into silence, tell me the rest. Another day, on getting into my train at the Flats, I missed from my pocket a volume of popular science—I think it was on some recent discoveries in biochemistry—which I had carried with me to read on the way. I thought no more about it till I got into the sleigh again that evening and Frome held out the book to me.

"I found it after you were gone," he said.

I put the volume into my pocket, and we lapsed into our usual silence; but as we began to crawl up the long hill from Corbury Flats to the Starkfield plateau I became aware through the dusk that Frome had turned his face to mine.

"There are things in that book that I didn't know the first word about," he said abruptly.

I was less surprised by his statement than by an odd note of resentment in his voice. He was evidently surprised and slightly aggrieved at his own ignorance. "Does that sort of thing interest you?" I asked.

"It used to," he answered.

"There are one or two rather new things in the book: there have been some big strides lately in that particular line of research." I waited a moment for a reply that did not come; then I said: "If you'd like to look the book through I'd be glad to leave it with you."

He hesitated, and I had the impression that he felt himself about to yield to a stealing tide of inertia; then, "Thank you—I'll take it," he answered briefly.

I hoped that this incident would establish some more direct communication between us. Frome was so devoid of vanity and self-assertion that I was sure his interest in the book was based on a genuine knowledge of its subject. The revelation of tastes and aptitudes so unexpected in a man of his condition made the contrast more poignant between his outer situation and his inner needs, and I argued that the rare chance of giving expression to the latter might at last unseal his lips. But I had reckoned without the inveterate habit of solitude. Something in the man's past, or in his present way of living, had apparently driven him too deeply into himself for any casual impulse to draw him back to contact with his kind. At our next meeting he made no allusion to the book, and our subsequent intercourse seemed fated to remain as negative and one-sided as if there had been no break in his reserve.

Frome had been driving me over to the Flats for about ten days when one morning I looked out of my window into a dense curtain of falling snow. From the height of the undulations dimly discerned against the garden-fence and down the empty street I saw that the storm must have been going on all night, and that the drifts would be exceptionally heavy in the open. I thought it probable that my train would be seriously delayed; but it was necessary that I should be at the power-house for an hour or two that afternoon, and I decided, if Frome turned up, to drive over to the Flats and wait there till the train came in. But I don't know why I put it in the conditional, for I never doubted that Frome would appear. He was not the kind of man to be turned from his business by any commotion of the elements; and at the appointed hour his cutter glided up through the snow like a stage-apparition behind thickening veils of gauze.

I was getting to know him too well to express either surprise or gratitude at his keeping his appointment in such rough weather; but I exclaimed in surprise as I saw him turn his horse in a direction opposite to that which we usually took.

"The railroad's blocked by a freight-train that got stuck in a drift below the Flats," he explained, as we jogged off through the stinging whiteness.

"But look here—where are you taking me, then?"

"Straight to the Junction, by the shortest way," he answered, pointing up School House hill with his whip.

"To the Junction—in this storm? But it's a good ten miles!"

"The bay'll do it if you give him time. You said you had some business there this afternoon. I'll see you get there."

He said it so quietly that I could only answer: "My dear fellow, you're doing me the biggest kind of a favour."

"That's all right," he rejoined.

Abreast of the School House the road forked, and we dipped steeply down a lane to the left between hemlock boughs bent close to their trunks by the load of snow. I had often walked that way on Sundays, and knew that the solitary roof showing through bare branches near the bottom of the hill was that of Frome's saw-mill. It looked exanimate enough, with its idle wheel looming spectrally above the black stream dashed with yellow-white spume, and its cluster of sheds sagging under the weight of the snow. Frome did not even turn his head as we drove by, and still in silence we began to mount the next slope. About a mile farther, on a road I had never travelled, we came to an orchard of starved apple-trees writhing up hill among outcroppings of slate that nuzzled up through the snow like animals pushing out their noses to breathe. Beyond the orchard, a field or two, their boundaries lost under drifts; and above them, huddled against the white immensities of land and sky, one of those lonely New England farm-houses that make the landscape lonelier.

"That's my place," said Frome, with a sideway jerk of his lame elbow; and in the distress and oppression of the scene I did not know what to answer. The snow had stopped, and a flash of pale sunlight exposed the house on the slope above us in all its plaintive ugliness. The black wraith of a deciduous creeper flapped from the porch, and the thin wooden walls, under their worn coat of paint, seemed actually to shiver in the wind that had risen with the ceasing of the snow.

"The house was bigger in my father's time: I had to take down the 'L' a while back," Frome continued, correcting with a twitch of the left rein the bay's evident intention of turning in through the broken-down gate.

I saw then that the unusually forlorn and stunted look of the house was partly due to the removal of what is known in New England as the 'L'; that long deep-roofed adjunct, usually at right angles to the main house, and connecting it, by way of the dairy, store-rooms and tool-house, with the wood-shed and cow-barn. Whether because of the symbolic sense of this function, the image it presents of a life visibly linked with the soil, and enclosing within itself the chief sources of warmth and sustenance, or whether merely because of the solace extracted from the thought that dwellers in that harsh climate can get to their morning work without braving the weather, it is certain that the 'ell' rather than the house itself seems to be the centre, the actual hearth-stone, of the New England farm.

Perhaps because of this connection of ideas, on which I had often pondered in my solitary walks about Starkfield, I heard a wistful note in Frome's words, and saw, in the diminished house, the image of his own mutilated body.

"We're kinder side-tracked here now, but there was considerable passing before the railroad was carried through to the Flats." He roused the lagging bay with another twitch; then, as if the mere sight of the house had let me so deeply into his confidence that all feint of reserve was vain, he added abruptly: "I've always set down the worst of mother's trouble to that. When she got the rheumatism she used to sit up there and watch the road by the hour; and one year, when they was six months mending the Bettsbridge pike after the floods, and Harmon Gow had to bring his stage round this way, she picked up so that she used to get down to the gate most days to see him. But after the trains begun running nobody come by to speak of, and mother never could get it through her head what had happened, and it preyed on her right along till she died."

As we turned into the Corbury road the snow came down again, cutting off our last glimpse of the lonely hillside and the lonelier house; and Frome's silence fell with it, letting down between us the old veil of reticence. This time the wind did not cease with the return of the snow. Instead, it sprang up to a gale which now and then tore a rent in the thick sky and showed us, in a pale sweep of sunlight, a landscape chaotically disguised. But the bay was as good as his master's word, and we struggled through to the Junction in time for me to keep my appointment.

In the afternoon the snow held off again, and the clear light in the west seemed to my inexperienced eye an assurance that the storm was over. I despatched my business as quickly as possible, and we set out on the return journey to Starkfield with a fair chance of getting there for supper. But at twilight the snow came on again, bringing an earlier night. This time it fell straight and steadily from a sky without wind, in a soft universal diffusion more confusing than the gusts and eddies of the morning: it seemed to be a part of the thickening darkness, to be the night itself descending on us, layer by layer.

The weak ray of Frome's lantern was soon lost in this smothering medium, in which even his sense of direction, and the bay's homing instinct, finally ceased to serve us. Twice or thrice some ghostly landmark sprang up to warn us that we were astray, and then was absorbed again into the mist; and when we finally regained our road the horse began to give signs of exhaustion. I felt myself to blame for having accepted Frome's offer, and after a brief argument I induced him to let me get out of the cutter and trudge along through the snow at the bay's side. In this fashion we struggled on for some distance, and finally reached a point where Frome, peering into what seemed to me formless night, said: "That's my gate down yonder."

The last mile had been the hardest part of the way. The bitter cold and the heavy going had nearly knocked the wind out of me, and I could feel the bay's flank heaving jerkily under my hand.

"Look here, Frome," I began, "there's no earthly use in your going any farther—" but he interrupted me: "Nor you neither. There's been about enough of this for anybody."

I understood that he was offering me a night's shelter, and without a word I turned in to the gate at his side, and following him into the barn, helped him to unharness and bed down the weary horse. Then he unhooked the lantern from the cutter, stepped out into the night, and said curtly, over his shoulder: "This way."

Far off above us a yellow square of light trembled through the snow. I floundered toward it after my guide, and in the blackness almost fell into the deep drift that had formed against the porch. Ethan scrambled up the steps ahead of me, kicking the snow aside with his heavily-booted foot. Then he lifted his lantern, found the latch, and opened the door. I followed him into a low unlit passage, at the back of which a flight of ladder-like stairs disappeared into obscurity. To the left, a line of light marked the door of the room which had sent its lamp-ray across the darkness. Behind the door I heard a woman's voice droning querulously. Frome shook the snow from his boots, and set down his lantern on a hollow-seated chair which was the only piece of furniture in the hall. Then he pushed open the door.

"Come in," he said to me; and as he spoke the woman's voice ceased.

It was that night that I found the clue to Ethan Frome, and had the vision of his story . . .

Introduction to the Modern Student's Library Edition of *Ethan Frome**

EDITH WHARTON's introduction to this student's edition of *Ethan Frome,* published eleven years after the story's original appearance, marked a break in her usual habit of reticence about her own work. It was in fact her first published comment on her method as a writer of fiction.

INTRODUCTION

I had known something of New England village life long before I made my home in the same country as my imaginary Starkfield; though, during the years spent there, certain of its aspects became much more familiar to me.

Even before that final initiation, however, I had had an uneasy sense that the New England of fiction bore little—except a vague botanical and dialectical—resemblance to the harsh and beautiful land as I had seen it. Even the abundant enumeration of sweet-fern, asters and mountain-laurel, and the conscientious reproduction of the vernacular, left me with the feeling that the outcropping granite had in both cases been overlooked. I give the impression merely as a personal one; it accounts for Ethan Frome, and may, to some readers, in a measure justify it.

So much for the origin of the story; there is noth-[v/vi]ing else of interest to say of it, except as concerns its construction.

The problem before me, as I saw in the first flash, was this: I had to deal with a subject of which the dramatic climax, or rather the anti-climax, occurs a generation later than the first acts of the tragedy. This enforced lapse of time would seem to anyone persuaded—as I have always been—that every subject (in the novelist's sense of the term) implicitly *contains its own form and dimensions,* to mark "Ethan Frome" as the subject for a novel. But I never thought this for a moment, for I had felt, at the same time, that the theme of my tale was not one on which many variations could be played. It must be treated as starkly and summarily as life had always presented itself to my protagonists; any attempt to elaborate and complicate their sentiments would necessarily have falsified the whole. They were, in truth, these figures, my *granite outcroppings;* but half-emerged from the soil, and scarcely more articulate.

This incompatibility between subject and plan [vi/vii] would perhaps have seemed to suggest that my "situation" was after all one to be rejected. Every novelist has been visited by the insinuating wraiths of false "good situations," siren-subjects luring his cockle-shell to the rocks; their voice is oftenest heard, and their mirage-sea beheld, as he traverses the waterless desert which awaits him half-way through whatever work is actually in hand. I knew well enough what song those sirens sang, and had often tied myself to my dull job till they were out of hearing—perhaps carrying a lost masterpiece in their rainbow veils. But I had no such fear of them in the case of Ethan Frome. It was the first subject I had ever approached with full confidence in its value, for my own pur-

* Edith Wharton, Introduction to The Modern Student's Library edition of *Ethan Frome* (New York: Charles Scribner's Sons, 1922), pp. v–x. Reprinted by permission of Charles Scribner's Sons.

pose, and a relative faith in my power to render at least a part of what I saw in it.

Every novelist, again, who "intends upon" his art, has lit upon such subjects, and been fascinated by the difficulty of presenting them in the fullest relief, yet without an added ornament, or a trick of drapery or lighting. This was my task, if I were to tell the story of Ethan Frome; and my scheme of [**vii/viii**] construction—which met with the immediate and unqualified disapproval of the few friends to whom I tentatively outlined it—I still think justified in the given case. It appears to me, indeed, that, while an air of artificiality is lent to a tale of complex and sophisticated people which the novelist causes to be guessed at and interpreted by any mere looker-on, there need be no such drawback if the looker-on is sophisticated, and the people he interprets are simple. If he is capable of seeing all around them, no violence is done to probability in allowing him to exercise this faculty; it is natural enough that he should act as the sympathizing intermediary between his rudimentary characters and the more complicated minds to whom he is trying to present them. But this is all self-evident, and needs explaining only to those who have never thought of fiction as an art of composition.

The real merit of my construction seems to me to lie in a minor detail. I had to find means to bring my tragedy, in a way at once natural and picture-making, to the knowledge of its narrator. I might [**viii/ix**] have sat him down before a village gossip who would have poured out the whole affair to him in a breath, but in doing this I should have been false to two essential elements of my picture: first, the deep-rooted reticence and inarticulateness of the people I was trying to draw, and secondly the effect of "roundness" (in the plastic sense) produced by letting their case be seen through eyes as different as those of Harmon Gow and Mrs. Ned Hale. Each of my chroniclers contributes to the narrative *just so much as he or she is capable of understanding* of what, to them, is a complicated and mysterious case; and only the narrator of the tale has scope enough to see it all, to resolve it back into simplicity, and to put it in its rightful place among his larger categories.

I make no claim for originality in following a method of which "La Grande Bretêche" and "The Ring and the Book" had set me the magnificent example; my one merit is, perhaps, to have guessed that the proceeding there employed was also applicable to my small tale.

I have written this brief analysis—the first I have [**ix/x**] ever published of any of my books—because, as an author's introduction to his work, I can imagine nothing of any value to his readers except a statement as to why he decided to attempt the work in question, and why he selected one form rather than another for its embodiment. These primary aims, the only ones that can be explicitly stated, must, by the artist, be almost instinctively felt and acted upon before there can pass into his creation that imponderable something more which causes life to circulate in it, and preserves it for a little from decay.

The Writing of *Ethan Frome**

EDITH WHARTON's brief account of the origin of *Ethan Frome*, written for a book collectors' quarterly, testifies to her lasting impatience with critics who questioned her knowledge of rural New England life. It was published near the end of her career, at a time when she was beginning the composition of her memoirs, subsequently to appear as *A Backward Glance* (1934).

The conditions in which *Ethan Frome* originated have remained much more clearly fixed in my memory than those connected with any of my other stories, owing to the odd accident of the tale's having been begun in French. Early in the nineteen hundreds I happened to be spending a whole winter in Paris, and it occurred to me to make use of the opportunity to polish and extend my conversational French; for though I had spoken the language since the age of four I had never had occasion to practise it for any length of time, at least with cultivated people, having frequently wandered through France as a tourist, but never lived there for more than a few weeks consecutively. Accordingly, it was arranged that I should read and talk for so many hours a week with a young French professor; and soon after our studies began he suggested that before each of his visits I should prepare an "exercise" for him.

I have never been able, without much mental anguish, to write anything but a letter or a story, and as stories come to me much more easily than letters, I timidly asked him if a story would "do," and, though obviously somewhat surprised at the unexpected suggestion, he acquiesced with equal timidity. Thus the French version of *Ethan Frome* began,

and ploughed its heavy course through a copy-book or two; then the lessons were interrupted and the Gallic "Ethan" abandoned, I forget at what point in his career. The copy-book containing this earliest version of his adventures has long since vanished; but a few years later Ethan's history stirred again in my memory, and I forthwith sat down and wrote it in English, reading aloud each evening what I had done during the day to a friend as familiar as I was with the lonely lives in half-deserted New England villages, before the coming of the motor and the telephone. The legend that Henry James suggested my transposing the French "composition" into an English tale—a fable I have frequently come across of recent years—must be classed among the other inventions which honour me by connecting my name with his in the field of letters. I am not sure if he even saw the French beginning of the tale, but he certainly did not suggest its rewriting in English, and never read the story, or heard of it again, till it appeared in print in the latter language.

While I am on the subject of literary fables, I might as well destroy another which likewise concerns *Ethan Frome*. Not long since I read a thoughtful article on the making of fiction, in which the author advanced the theory that in a

* Edith Wharton, "The Writing of *Ethan Frome*," *The Colophon: The Book Collectors' Quarterly*, Number 11 (September 1932). [There are no page numbers in *The Colophon*.]

given case a certain perspective might be necessary to the novelist, and that one might conceivably write a better book about Main Street if one lived as far away from it as Paris or Palermo; in proof of which *Ethan Frome* was cited as an instance of a successful New England story written by some one who knew nothing of New England. I have no desire to contest the theory, with which, in a certain measure, I am disposed to agree; but the fact is that *Ethan Frome* was written after a ten years' residence in the New England hill country where Ethan's tragedy was enacted, and that during those years I had become very familiar with the aspect, the dialect and the general mental attitude of the Ethans, Zeenas and Mattie Silvers of the neighbouring villages. My other short novel of New England life, *Summer,* which deals with the same type of people involved in a different tragedy of isolation, might, one would suppose, have helped to prove to the legend-makers that I knew something at first hand of the life and the people into whose intimacy I had asked my readers to enter with me on two successive occasions.

[The Genesis of *Ethan Frome*] *

EDITH WHARTON published her autobiography, *A Backward Glance* (1934), three years before her death. It is an engaging but reticent account of her early career, her travels, and, most important, her friendships; its tone is marked by a polite aversion to the post-war world and a qualified nostalgia for the world of her youth.

. . . .
. . . The book to the making of which I brought the greatest joy and the fullest ease was "Ethan Frome". For years I had wanted to draw life as it really was in the derelict mountain villages of New England, a life even in my time, and a thousandfold more a generation earlier, utterly unlike that seen through the rose-coloured spectacles of my predecessors, Mary Wilkins and Sarah Orne Jewett. In those days the snow-bound vil-[**293/294**]lages of Western Massachusetts were still grim places, morally and physically: insanity, incest and slow mental and moral starvation were hidden away behind the paintless wooden house-fronts of the long village street, or in the isolated farm-houses on the neighbouring hills; and Emily Brontë would have found as savage tragedies in our remoter valleys as on her Yorkshire moors. In this connection, I may mention that every detail about the colony of drunken mountain outlaws described in "Summer" was given to me by the rector of the church at Lenox (near which we lived), and that the lonely peak I have called "the Mountain" was in reality Bear Mountain, an isolated summit not more than twelve miles from our own home. The rector had been fetched there by one of the mountain outlaws to read the Burial Service over a woman of

evil reputation; and when he arrived every one in the house of mourning was drunk, and the service was performed as I have related it. The rector's predecessor in the fashionable parish of Lenox had, I believe, once been called for on a similar errand, but had prudently refused to go; my friend, however, thought it his duty to do so, and drove off alone with the outlaw—coming back with his eyes full of horror and his heart of anguish and pity. Needless to say, when "Summer" appeared, this chapter was received with indignant denial by many reviewers and readers; and not the least vociferous were the New Englanders who had for years sought the reflection of local life in the rose-and-lavender pages of their favourite authoresses—and had forgotten to look into Hawthorne's. [**294/295**]

"Ethan Frome" shocked my readers less than "Summer"; but it was frequently criticized as "painful", and at first had much less success than my previous books. I have a clearer recollection of its beginnings than of those of my other tales, through the singular accident that its first pages were written—in French! I had determined, when we came to live in Paris, to polish and enlarge my French vocabulary; for though I had spoken the language since the age of four I had never had much occasion to talk it, for any length of time, with cultivated people, having usually, since my marriage, wandered through France as a tourist. The result was that I had kept up the language chiefly through reading, and the favourite French authors of my early youth being Bossuet, Racine, Corneille and La Bruyère, most of my polite locutions dated from the seventeenth century, and Bourget used to laugh at me for speaking "the purest Louis Quatorze". To bring my idioms up to date I asked Charles Du Bos to find, among his friends, a young professor who would come and talk with me two or three times a week. An amiable young man was found; but, being too amiable ever to correct my spoken mistakes, he finally hit on the expedient of asking me to prepare an "exercise" before each visit. The easiest thing for me was to write a story; and thus the French version of "Ethan Frome" was begun, and carried on for a few weeks. Then the lessons were given up, and the copy-book containing my "exercise" vanished forever. But a few years later, during one of our summer sojourns at the Mount, a distant glimpse of Bear Mountain brought Ethan back to my memory, and the [**295/296**] following winter in Paris I wrote the tale as it now stands, reading my morning's work aloud each evening to Walter Berry, who was as familiar as I was with the lives led in those half-deserted villages before the coming of motor and telephone. We talked the tale over page by page, so that its accuracy of "atmosphere" is doubly assured—and I mention this because not long since, in an article by an American literary critic, I saw "Ethan Frome" cited as an interesting example of a successful New England story written by some one who knew nothing of New England! "Ethan Frome" was written after I had spent ten years in the hill-region where the scene is laid, during which years I had come to know well the aspect, dialect, and mental and moral attitude of the hill-people. The fact that "Summer" deals with the same class and type as those portrayed in "Ethan Frome", and has the same setting, might have sufficed to disprove the legend—but once such a legend is started it echoes on as long as its subject survives. . . .

The Writing of Fiction*

EDITH WHARTON's manual on the fiction writer's craft, *The Writing of Fiction* (1925), is a compact general statement of the basic principles governing the composition of the short story and the novel. It owes something to Henry James's theories of the well-made novel, but more to Mrs. Wharton's wide and intelligent reading in British and continental fiction.

It is sometimes said that a "good subject" for a short story should always be capable of being expanded into a novel.

The principle may be defendable in special cases; but it is certainly a misleading one on which to build any general theory. Every "subject" (in the novelist's sense of the term) must necessarily contain within itself its own dimensions; and one of the fiction-writer's essential gifts is that of discerning whether the subject which presents itself to him, asking for incarnation, is suited to the proportions of a short story or of a novel. If it appears to be adapted to both the chances are that it is inadequate to either.

It would be as great a mistake, however, to try to base a hard-and-fast theory on the denial of the rule as on its assertion. Instances [**41/42**] of short stories made out of subjects that could have been expanded into a novel, and that are yet typical short stories and not mere stunted novels, will occur to every one. General rules in art are useful chiefly as a lamp in a mine, or a hand-rail down a black stairway; they are necessary for the sake of the guidance they give, but it is a mistake, once they are formulated, to be too much in awe of them.

There are at least two reasons why a subject should find expression in novel-form rather than as a tale; but neither is based on the number of what may be conveniently called incidents, or external happenings, which the narrative contains. There are novels of action which might be condensed into short stories without the loss of their distinguishing qualities. The marks of the subject requiring a longer development are, first, the gradual unfolding of the inner life of its characters, and secondly the need of producing in the reader's mind the sense of the lapse of time. Outward events of the most [**42/43**] varied and exciting nature may without loss of probability be crowded into a few hours, but moral dramas usually have their roots deep in the soul, their rise far back in time; and the suddenest-seeming clash in which they culminate should be led up to step by step if it is to explain and justify itself.

There are cases, indeed, when the short story may make use of the moral drama at its culmination. If the incident dealt with be one which a single retrospective flash sufficiently lights up, it is qualified for use as a short story; but if the subject be so complex, and its successive phases so interesting, as to justify elaboration, the lapse of time must necessarily be suggested, and the novel-form becomes appropriate.

The effect of compactness and instantaneity sought in the short story is attained mainly by the observance of two

* Edith Wharton, section III from "Telling a Short Story," *The Writing of Fiction* (New York: Charles Scribner's Sons, 1925), pp. 41–46. Copyright 1925 Charles Scribner's Sons; renewal copyright 1953 William R Tyler. Reprinted by permission of Charles Scribner's Sons.

"unities"—the old traditional one of time, and that other, more modern and complex, which requires that any rapidly enacted episode shall be seen through only one pair of eyes. [**43/44**]

It is fairly obvious that nothing is more retarding than the marking of a time-interval long enough to suggest modification in the personages of the tale or in their circumstances. The use of such an interval inevitably turns the short story into a long tale unduly compressed, the bald scenario of a novel. In the third chapter, where an attempt will be made to examine the technique of the novel, it will be needful to explore that central mystery—of which Tolstoy was perhaps the one complete master—the art of creating in the reader's mind this sense of passing time. Meanwhile, it may be pointed out that a third, and intermediate form of tale—the *long* short-story—is available for any subject too spreading for conciseness yet too slight in texture to be stretched into a novel.

The other unity, that of vision, will also be dealt with in considering the novel, in respect of which it becomes a matter much more complicated. Henry James, almost the only novelist who has formulated his ideas [**44/45**] about his art, was the first to lay down the principle, though it had long (if intermittently) been observed by the masters of fiction. It may have occurred to other novelists—presumably it has—to ask themselves, as they sat down to write: Who saw this thing I am going to tell about? By whom do I mean that it shall be reported? It seems as though such a question must precede any study of the subject chosen, since the subject is conditioned by the answer; but no critic appears to have propounded it, and it was left to Henry James to do so in one of those entangled prefaces to the Definitive Edition from which the technical axioms ought some day to be piously detached.

It is clear that exactly the same thing never happens to any two people, and that each witness of a given incident will report it differently. Should some celestial task-master set the same theme to Jane Austen and George Meredith the bewildered reader would probably have some difficulty in discovering the common denominator. Henry [**45/46**] James, in pointing this out, also made the corollary suggestion that the mind chosen by the author to mirror his given case should be so situated, and so constituted, as to take the widest possible view of it.

One thing more is needful for the ultimate effect of probability; and that is, never to let the character who serves as reflector record anything not naturally within his register. It should be the story-teller's first care to choose this reflecting mind deliberately, as one would choose a building-site, or decide upon the orientation of one's house, and when this is done, to live inside the mind chosen, trying to feel, see and react exactly as the latter would, no more, no less, and, above all, no otherwise. Only thus can the writer avoid attributing incongruities of thought and metaphor to his chosen interpreter.

PART THREE

THE COMMENTATORS

The Novels of Edith Wharton*

PERCY LUBBOCK (1879–1965) was an English novelist, essayist, and historian, best known in this country for his distinguished treatise on the novel, *The Craft of Fiction* (1921). He was a close friend of Edith Wharton and Henry James (whose letters he edited in 1920) and of such members of their circle as Bernard Berenson, Geoffrey Scott, Howard Sturgis, and Mrs. Wharton's first literary executor, Gaillard Lapsley. His *Portrait of Edith Wharton* (1947), a collaborative memoir written with the aid of Mrs. Wharton's friends, is one of the few sources of biographical information about the novelist. Among Lubbock's other books are *Earlham* (1922), the story of his grandparents' house in Norfolk, and two novels, *Roman Pictures* (1923) and *The Region Cloud* (1925).

. . . Meanwhile, directly facing the full glare of the relentless American light, comes the grim little story called 'Ethan Frome.' Here indeed is American life of a tougher substance than that of Fifth Avenue, life as tightly wedged in its snow-piled mountain-valleys as the other drifts aimlessly. In such a setting the simplest notes fall sharply on a wintry silence which seems to be waiting for unrelieved and fantastic tragedies like Ethan's. The bitter futilities which imprison Ethan's existence close on it again faster than ever after his one crowning and vain attempt to bring passion, if not to life, at least to death. Not only is the gift of death denied to Ethan and Mattie, but they may not even live in an undesecrated memory of their single contact with beauty. By the long anti-climax of their fate memory itself is corroded; and it is the mean indignity of pain, not its sanctity, which is thrown upon Ethan's tragic powers of endurance.

There is no prescribing the limitations of a talent which never tires of the enterprise of criticism. Mrs Wharton's art, trained on all the refinements and sophistications of modernity, rose in 'Ethan Frome' to meet suggestions of an entirely new kind and instantly singled out their peculiar demand. We can see in the finished tale exactly what this demand was and how easy it would have been to overlook it. Ethan's history was just a flash of inarticulate passion, thrown against the blinding whiteness of the New England winter. There are no half-tones in such a life, and nothing for the writer to do—so it might seem, but to give with as few strokes as possible the huge monotony of the [**193/194**] snow and the brief storm of Ethan's rebellion. The story would need only the telling juxtaposition of two such intense effects. It would be a drama, but a drama of landscape, the dumbness of these village tragedies being such as to make them appear but a part, even a subordinate part, of the scene—mountain or field or forest—which witnesses them. We have had a good deal of this decorative treatment of village life, and America seems to have had still more; but we have not had much of the sort that Mrs. Wharton gives us. 'Ethan Frome' is not in the least a study in *genre*. Its landscape is there, and there with all vividness, but it is behind it. The action in front, the strange calamitous issue, has its perfectly independent movement. It is

* Percy Lubbock, from "The Novels of Edith Wharton," *Quarterly Review*, CCXXIII (January 1915), 182–201.

not described for the sake of the picturesque scene; the scene is described, the snow blazes, for the sake of the action. How, then, was Ethan's story, where there is so little that can happen and so much less still that can be spoken in words, to be made to stand out and take the eye with its own dramatic value? This, as Mrs Wharton has seen, is the appeal of the story to such art as hers, for which a mere 'landscape with figures' would be too easy to be interesting. She meets the appeal in a manner more difficult to define than to recognise and admire.

What is it, in fact, which makes the slightest, most trivial incident seem, under certain hands, to glow with an inner light, to appear unique and final and incomparable with anything else, so that we do not think of weighing or measuring it by any general standard? The little characteristic episode, chosen by the novelist to illustrate some development of a situation, may become, if it has this quality, a poem of delight, where, if the quality is lacking, we are only irritated by the transparency of the novelist's art. The great master of this particular subtlety is undoubtedly Tolstoi, with his extraordinary power of absorbing the whole of our attention with a few light touches, till the scene evoked grows important and urgent, a thing to be watched breathlessly, even though it may be no more than the picture of a stable-boy saddling a horse or a child amusing itself with a box of paints. Whatever it consists in, this power is at work in 'Ethan [194/195] Frome.' The tiny incidents which lead gradually up to the strange catastrophe are magnetised and luminous and *quick*. We do not feel that Mrs Wharton, in telling her story by means of such small homely events, is using a clever artistic restraint; we feel, on the contrary, that the events—a tramp through the snow, the breaking of a glass dish, the carrying of a trunk downstairs—are the natural and sufficient channels of great emotion. How is it done? The question touches what is perhaps the central and most distinguishing gift of the true novelist, his power of so completely identifying himself with the character through whose eyes he is seeing that his field of vision, both in extent and in particularity, is exactly no more and no less than that of the man or woman he has imagined. Mrs Wharton, in the few and simple pages of 'Ethan Frome,' has shown more conclusively that she possesses this power than in anything else she has written, for she has written nothing in which she has so rigorously denied herself all other help. . . .

Idealized New England*

ELIZABETH SHEPLEY SERGEANT (1881–1965), born in Massachusetts and for many years a resident of Paris, published her first book, *French Perspectives*, in 1916. A close friend of many of the major writers of her generation, she wrote *Fire Under the Andes* (1927), a collection of portrait-essays on Mencken, Frost, O'Neill, and others; *Willa Cather: A Memoir* (1953), based on her long friendship with the novelist; and an authorized biography of another old friend, *Robert Frost: The Trial by Existence* (1960), on the revision of which she was engaged when she died.

"What a terrible book," I said, "what a supremely cruel book!"

"A tragic masterpiece," she contradicted, "a landmark in American literature. Against that iron New England background Mrs. Wharton's few figures have an almost Euripidean quality."

"But the Greeks never made their audiences writhe," I protested. "Could you write choruses to 'Ethan Frome,' melodious choruses to be chanted by tranquil, veiled women and offering some alleviation to the bitter lot of man? No," I went on with heat, "you'll find only jibbering fiends to break Ethan's agony. The story is a fine example of what hate can accomplish as creative inspiration; and of the difference between observation and understanding."

"Come now," she said, "that sounds like local prejudice. You should be sufficiently disaffected by New York and Europe to perceive the depleted side of your native states."

"Have I not seen the industrious Swede and the inscrutable Finn absorbing the land cleared by my ancestors' vitality?"

"Well then! And you care so much for the French classic manner—how can you fail to appreciate the rapidity, the suppressions, the sharp yet delicate shadings of this poignant New England drama?"

"Ah, but that's just why the book wounds me so. My acquired literary sense, which Mrs. Wharton pricks to admiration on every page, here conflicts with something far more real and subconscious—the knowledge I was born with of the kind of people, the kind of place, yes and the kind of drama of weakened will she is so relentlessly describing. And I tell you that in spite of the *vraisemblance* of the surface, she has got them all wrong. She has nowhere dug down into the subsoil."

"You don't mind quarreling with the authorities," she remarked. "Of course you read Mr. Herrick on Mrs. Wharton in THE NEW REPUBLIC?"

"Yes, it was precisely that article which sent me back to the sources. No doubt Mrs. Wharton is more psychologist than social historian; no doubt, as he said, her real interest is in the subtler and more universal sort of spiritual conflicts. But I can't admit that the conflict between love and duty in 'Ethan Frome' is less conditioned by special environment, than, for example, Lily Bart's struggle."

"You will grant that men tied to wives older than themselves, ill, ugly and querulous, are doomed in every quarter of the globe to fall in love with girls like black-

* Elizabeth Shepley Sergeant, "Idealized New England," *New Republic*, III (May 8, 1915), 20–21. Reprinted by permission of the Elizabeth Shepley Sergeant Estate.

berries who put red ribbons in their hair."

"Certainly. But Ethan and his wife Zeena, and her young cousin, Mattie Silver, are not generalized types. Would Mr. Herrick accept them as they stand, for Ohio or Illinois? They are New England country people of old stock living in a lonely snowed-in hill town in the Berkshires. Mrs. Wharton's deliberate purpose is to show what life in Starkfield really means to a man who has been there too many winters; to show the grim New England skeleton that the summer resident usually fails to discover during his pleasant months in the elm-shaded village—unless he happens upon a degenerate chore-boy, or sees a poor little girl in short skirts carrying her shame to school under a cape."

"True, and the New England writers have largely ignored the skeleton. The 'idyll' has been done to death, like the conscience. I commend Mrs. Wharton for finding a new subject in an overworked field."

"So do I, but if 'Ethan Frome' is a New England tale in the same sense as Miss Brown's or Mrs. Freeman's stories or 'The Country of the Pointed Firs'— and this is just the point I am venturing to make against Mr. Herrick—then surely one is justified in asking, as he does about the New York novels, whether the author has been fair to her subject. Do Zeena's false teeth click true, do Ethan and Mattie make love in Starkfield fashion, would they have taken the fatal coast that brought about the intolerable horror of their lives?"

"Ugh," said my friend, "those false teeth—what a sure realistic note! I can never forget the glass by the bed, into which the wife dropped them when she blew out the candle at night in the terrible gray, cold room."

"Of course you can't. Neither could Mrs. Wharton. You both look at Starkfield with the eyes of the sophisticated stranger who arrives there in a blizzard, and stumbles through the drifts into Ethan's run-down 'place.' You notice the superficial things that would make you miserable. Ethan suffered in all sorts of ways, but not from false teeth: he was brought up on them! His mother had them; his cousins and neighbors had them; he probably admired Mattie less because she hadn't 'had her molars out'!"

"Well, I waive the teeth," said she with a shudder. "Let's take the coasting parties and the church sociable. Surely Mrs. Wharton has those in key?"

"In the unconsciously contemptuous key of the person who has a box at the opera. How should cosmopolitans understand what such diversions mean to Starkfield folks? They have all sorts of consolations if you only knew. Even when winter breaks and the teams sink up to their axles in mud, they have things to live for and look for—pussy-willows, for instance. Laugh if you like! Do you remember 'Miss Tempy's Watchers' and the one thorny quince tree she 'kind of expected into bloomin' ' every spring?"

"You mean that because of its very repressions, its very barrenness, and physical deprivations, New England life still produces a sort of flower—"

"Pale as snowdrops, hidden in dead leaves like hepaticas and arbutus; yet precious to those who know where to look for it. That is the sort of flower Ethan's and Mattie's love was, but they could never have expressed it to each other."

"Mrs. Wharton lets them express it so little," she objected.

"Ah, but a word, a touch would have spoiled it for them. I think Ethan, dim and weakened descendant of rugged forefathers that he was, would have had the spirit to drive his Mattie to the station when his wife sent her packing. But he would not have dreamed of stopping for that preposterous coast for death. It was just Mrs. Wharton's own sense of the blankness and emptiness, the lack of beauty and passion in Starkfield lives, that made her construct that tremendous fourth act for her lovers and condemn them to its gruesome, long-drawn epilogue."

"You think they would have driven on silently to the station and parted with a dumb handshake and a look?"

"Sustained by something they did not understand, something they half rebelled against and yet could not possibly foreswear."

"Then Ethan's real tragedy would have been that he had nothing real, tangible, to cling to—only an idea, a feeling, a dream to carry him through those slow gray years when Zeena continued to flourish on patent medicines?"

"Exactly. The real New England tragedy, as Mrs. Wharton herself realized at bottom, is not that something happens but that nothing does. Yet if Ethan was tender to Zeena instead of strangling her complaining voice in her lanky throat, it was because when he was out alone in the [20/21] pasture lot and heard the hermit thrush singing in the pines he knew he had been right. The image of his girl was warm in his heart then and undefiled, like Martha's memory of her 'lady.' "

"Miss Jewett again! It isn't fair. She had a natural love of light and sun, an aversion to the shadow and cruelty and ugliness of life which Mrs. Wharton has the courage to face and to probe."

"Is that the essential point of difference? I don't think so. There are chapters in Miss Jewett's works—in 'Deephaven' for example—and passages in her letters which show her full knowledge of the shadow even though she did not often linger there. For that matter, almost any of her stories if told from outside in rather than from inside out might be sordid and grim. That's the bearing of our whole argument, isn't it? Take the 'The Queen's Twin.' What was she? To most people a poor, cracked old creature, the victim of a silly delusion. It needed the feeling heart of Mrs. Todd to realize that she was, in fact as in fancy, the sister soul of royalty, a woman with a shining destiny."

"You evidently think the only creative truth is that perceived by love. I believe any strong passion is worth recording."

"Possibly. Indifference could not have written 'Ethan Frome.' But if Mrs. Wharton had realized Ethan as Miss Jewett did the Queen's Twin, as she herself loved and understood her most significant creation, Lily Bart, we should get some shock of those deep-down unwritable things which are the vital parts of novels as they are of human beings. We should get life, not a literary copy of it."

"It's no use," said my friend, "to argue on her own soil with the descendant of a band of hopeless idealists who see the hardest facts in a sort of Platonic glow. I am afraid I must still read and admire 'Ethan Frome.' "

"Wait till you are old. That is a New England counsel, but just wait! Then the 'Queen's Twin,' and the 'Dunnet Shepherdess' will still be full of living human poetry and truth and the salt-sweet scent of high coast pastures, and 'Ethan Frome' will be rotting in his grave."

[Edith Wharton and George Eliot]*

OSBERT BURDETT (1885–1936) was an English essayist, dramatist, and critic; author of *The Beardsley Period* (1925), *Critical Essays* (1925), *The Art of Living* (1933), and studies of William Blake, Browning, and the Carlyles.

. . . .
. . . [*Ethan Frome*] is noticeably concise when compared with its forerunners, and its concern is with the permanent, not the temporary, attributes of human nature. It is a tale with a beginning, a middle, and an end. It is dramatic and arresting. It is simple. As a work of art it can be compared with *Silas Marner,* and that is high praise. But just as *Silas Marner* was, even in its title, too literary to be great literature, too like a study of peasant life from a scholar's window to be a living image of the countryside, so *Ethan Frome,* as its name too implies, is a structure rather than a creation. The very virtues in which such constructions abound are betrayals of their origin. We must admire, we hesitate to love, them. The gaunt silent figure of Ethan, moved by the circumstances of his lonely life to make an unfortunate marriage with a grim and shrewish woman, is a type after George Eliot's own heart. He turns to the poor relation who comes to live with him and his wife in return for ceaseless service, as a sunflower to the single beam that falls his way. When his wife drives her from the house on what all three silently understand to be a jealous pretext, the failure that attends his attempt to commit a joint suicide with the young woman, and the continued existence of the three in unspoken bitterness is the tragedy of their interminable lives. But whereas George Eliot's language was apt to be heavy, Mrs. Wharton's touch is by comparison light. It cannot be said truthfully of her, as of George Eliot, that there is too much suet in her style. She is direct and lucid, though her characters are somewhat stiff. The abortive accident with the sleigh is a transparent artifice. Its telling does not bring conviction to the feelings, but Ethan Frome seems nearer to simple human nature than any of her previous characters, though even he is a projection [57/58] less of intuition than of thought. The story holds, and it is only on reflection that we question the freshness of its springs. The introductory chapters plod, a little in the manner of the Brontë openings. The personal scenes between Ethan and Mrs. Frome, the scenes indeed in which the wife figures, are the best in the book. Mrs. Frome is the creation of the story; the girl is hardly individualised; Ethan is an echo of other voices. But, in the kind to which it belongs, it is excellent. Here, as elsewhere, whatever of construction can be acquired, its author has mastered. She has her craft, at least, at her fingers' ends. In her novels we see the European tradition of the art of prose narrative essaying to master the contrast of life in the States. When American literature is ripe for its historian, and he comes to examine its origins, say in 2125, he will see in Mrs. Wharton's narratives a talent derived from and nourished by the

* Osbert Burdett, from "Contemporary American Authors: Edith Wharton," *London Mercury*, XIII (November 1925), 52–61. Reprinted in *Contemporary American Authors*, edited by J. C. Squire (New York: Henry Holt & Company, 1928).

models of the Old World. She is a literary Pilgrim Father, with a lusty brood of native-bred descendants latent in her books. She is a founder of a family, not strictly an autochthonous American author herself.

. . . .

Characters and Character*

JOHN CROWE RANSOM (1888–) is one of America's most distinguished poets and critics. For many years he was an influential teacher, first at Vanderbilt, where he was a leader among the southern group of writers known as The Fugitives, and later at Kenyon College, where in 1938 he founded *The Kenyon Review*. His critical essays, collected in part in *The World's Body* (1938) and *The New Criticism* (1941), helped establish the New Criticism, that vigorous and many-headed movement which, following World War II, greatly influenced the study of literature in American colleges and universities.

I. *Mrs. Wharton's Difficulty*

If the tenth and last of the Muses is the patroness of fiction, that must have been the power who imposed upon the accomplished Mrs. Wharton a baffling professional responsibility. So it came to pass that Edith Wharton, tutored by no less a technician than Henry James, expert in her rendering of the smart scene and the better sort nearest to her, must spend a time in the Massachusetts back country which was quite long enough to make her sensible of a new scene and set of characters, and to acquaint her with a local tragedy that clamoured to be told. How should she tell it? We must judge from the odd structural pattern of *Ethan Frome,* as well as from its unsatisfactory detail, that the problem gave her trouble. We are told as much in the Preface. It is an honest Preface, and only slightly disingenuous.

To these natives of Starkfield Mrs. Wharton must have been something of a foreign wonder; classifiable, being a "New York lady", yet a strange and outland personage. She evidently struck herself, too, as alien to the mind of the Starkfielders, in fact to a degree that threatened to inhibit her representation of Ethan, who was a particularly grim and taciturn one of them. Who should tell Ethan's story? For there must be means to bring his story, "in a way at once natural [271/272] and picture-making, to the knowledge of its narrator", and through the narrator to the knowledge of the readers. If Ethan should tell it himself, it would not be identifiable with the main body of Mrs. Wharton's fiction. But if she should tell it, it would very likely be the story of a rather metamorphosed Ethan.

Says Mrs. Wharton of her harsh tragic plot and her strong silent actors:

> The theme of my tale was not one on which many variations could be played. It must be treated as starkly and summarily as life had always presented itself to my protagonists; any attempt to elaborate and complicate their sentiments would necessarily have falsified the whole. They were, in truth, these figures, my *granite outcroppings;* but half-emerged from the soil, and scarcely more articulate.

Of what use in a case like this was her trained and sophisticated sensibility? It was that which would have falsified the whole.

Mrs. Wharton compromised; or rather,

* John Crowe Ransom, from "Characters and Character: A Note on Fiction," *American Review*, VI (January 1936), 271–288. Reprinted by permission of the author.

since she did not thoroughly reform her usual practice, she temporized. She invented a special reporter for Ethan in the person of a young man of sensibility and education very like her own. In theory it gained her this, that the reporter became a man; and this, that not being herself he need not render quite the complete spiritual history of events associated with her name as an author. In effect, it gained her very little. Spiritually, this gentleman is cousin to the gentlemen who relate stories for Joseph Conrad and Willa Cather, and he could probably trace descent from one ghost writer or another who had been in Henry James's own employ. She makes for him a temporary resi-[**272/273**]dence in Starkfield and acquaints him with Ethan, at a time just twenty-four years after the event that is the heart of Ethan's story. How can he participate in it? He gets nothing out of Ethan, and only scraps of information out of the villagers, but manages finally to find himself snow-bound for the night at Ethan's house. Now Ethan's story is of a man, a wife, and an extra woman, and in Ethan's kitchen the reporter actually finds these three characters, still surviving, dumb and wretched, in the most enduring triangle that fiction has recorded. The scene is illuminating. But we catch only a glimpse of it. The reporter finds the illumination much before we do, and begins at once to spin the story, starting the twenty-four years back. To put together "this version of the story"; the phrase being followed by three rows of points or ellipses, and Chapter One. The story which we have heard of, and despaired of, has begun. It goes on. After nine chapters it is complete, externally with respect to events, and internally with respect to Ethan's mind. It sees Ethan just past the tragic smash. The last word is followed, in my edition, by four rows of ellipses and the resumption of the sketchy account of how the reporter later ferreted out the outlines of the story he has already told.

This is fairly remarkable, though not unique, since we have stories from Conrad which play similar tricks. We are allowed to anticipate the reporter who is gathering the story, and then we go back and see him make slight detective motions at gathering it; but we are forced to conclude that he did not gather it really; that, mostly, he made it up. Why a special reporter at all? And why such a peculiar chronological [**273/274**] method? These are features which picture to me, if it is not impertinent, the perturbation of an author wrestling with an unaccustomed undertaking, uneasy of conscience, and resorting to measures.

Forgetting the Preface, and the exterior or enveloping story, we attend strictly to Ethan's story, and discover that the fictitious reporter has had the goodness to enter Ethan's own mind and present events under the form of a focussed and continuous inner experience. That is, we are made to identify our own existence with Ethan's and to live his story with him. Or we are expected to, but to the best of my knowledge we cannot quite do it, we cannot become naturalized in Ethan's world. The tone is not always Ethan's, I think, imagining I know him better than Mrs. Wharton does. For instance:

> Well, she could go back to her people, then, and see what they would do for her. It was the fate she was forcing on Mattie—why not let her try it herself? By the time she had discovered his whereabouts, and brought suit for divorce, he would probably—wherever he was—be earning enough to pay her a sufficient alimony. And the alternative was to let Mattie go forth alone, with far less hope of ultimate provision.

Much is doubtful here; the alimony business would suit Mrs. Wharton's usual run of well-placed characters far better than this countrified Ethan; and the vocabulary. But beyond these positive discords there is the feeling that, identified with Ethan, we are not having quite as much sheer experience as the events would entitle us to have; and reflecting upon this, we first recall, and then reject, Mrs. Wharton's intimation (the prefatory one) that Ethan did not have [**274/275**] any complicated experience to record. The suspicion arises that, rather than this, Mrs. Wharton is merely not familiar with Ethan's variety of complications. The book is half long enough, or less; it is a "study", a well-proportioned first-draft or outline for the real circumstantial thing that was to come, that would have been fiction.

In view of Mrs. Wharton's successes with her own sort of material it will not be invidious to point to this relative failure, a case illustrating a difficulty that besets the conscientious author. Henry James himself would have failed in this particular undertaking; or if not, it is because his sense of tactics would not have permitted him to try it. . . .

Mrs. Wharton's predicament is this: she does not want to leave her own mentality too far, she is not at all sure that she will be at home in a strange one, so that she makes the change reluctantly; but she feels the necessity of entering Ethan's mentality, if his story is to be told, and in fact the necessity is imperative. It is commanded by her literary conscience. Clearly and sternly conscience says to the authors of fiction: Identify yourself with your characters. . . .

Introduction (1938) to *Ethan Frome**

BERNARD DE VOTO (1879–1956), teacher, historian, novelist, and critic, was one of America's best known and most controversial literary figures in the thirties and forties. He published fiction under the pseudonym "John August," edited the *Saturday Review of Literature* for two years (1936–38), wrote a column for *Harper's Magazine* (1935–52), and was curator of the Mark Twain literary estate. Among his works are *Mark Twain's America* (1932); *The Literary Fallacy* (1944), an attack on American writing of the twenties and thirties; and three books on western history, *The Year of Decision: 1846* (1943), *Across the Wide Missouri* (1947), and *The Course of Empire* (1952).

In her autobiography, Mrs. Wharton says that when she wrote *Ethan Frome* she felt for the first time the artisan's full control of his implements. She adds that its earliest reviewers severely criticized the book "for what was considered the clumsy structure," and goes on to dissent from their criticism. She then adds, most revealingly, "though I am far from thinking *Ethan Frome* my best novel, and am bored and even exasperated when I am told that it is, I am still sure that its structure is not its weak point."

Boredom one can understand: no artist is much interested in casual attempts to appraise his work by graded scale. But exasperation is something else; such vehemence may be protective and may supply a clue not only to Mrs. Wharton's own appraisal of her work but also to a doubt of it or at least a defence. Since she belonged to a generation when writers still had personal dignity, it can be no more [v/vi] than a clue; she has told us much about her craftsmanship but nothing whatever about the emotional charge it conducts. But she is exasperated by being told that her best book is her best book. Why? If she considered that *Ethan Frome* has a weak point, what is it? What

does it possess or what does it lack in comparison with her other work? One is free to speculate.

Now it may well be that when the present cycle of opinion has run out and our liveliest criteria of today look as quaint as any Godey print, the qualities of her other novels that were once held virtuous and admirable will reassert themselves. It seems altogether likely that, after the usual first-generation eclipse, *In Old New York,* for instance, will be more respected than it is now if only as a period piece done with discriminating sympathy, and *The Custom of the Country* and other studies of the plutocracy vanquishing the old aristocracy will recapture a considerable esteem. If so, criticism will to that extent be vindicating Mrs. Wharton's judgment. She regarded them as her best work and it is not hard to see why. They are the books in which her own experience is engaged, in which the artist has [vi/vii] a personal rather than a purely professional relationship to the material of her art. They contain what she has to tell about life in terms of experience rather than that ill-defined and subtly counterfeit quality which the salons and café tables call observation. Mrs. Wharton had a fine taste for irony but she could not enjoy a public judgment that her craftsmanship was better than her substance, that a book clearly unwarmed by the participation of the artist was worth more than the books in which her basic values were involved.

Yet the public judgment stands, and it is unlikely that a future revaluation of her other books will challenge the priority of *Ethan Frome*. Her greatest achievement is one of technical expertness and she is most respected not as an artist but as a professional writer. *Ethan Frome* is a model of literary technique but it is not a transcript of human experience; it is a "well-made" novel done with exact calculation and superb skill, but it is not an exploration of or comment on genuine emotion. It is, in short, literally a masterpiece, an exhibition of flawless craftsmanship by a writer who has learned all there is to learn about her trade. [**vii/viii**]

In an article published in *The Colophon* for September, 1932, and reprinted in Elmer Adler's anthology, *Breaking into Print,* Mrs. Wharton tells how the book came to be written. It was actually begun as an exercise in French composition—a circumstance which should satisfy the most exacting requirements of the "detachment" which was the catchword of the *fin de siècle* novelists under whose influence, as transmitted by Henry James, she had begun her career. The French lessons were abandoned before the story was finished and several years passed before "Ethan's history stirred in my memory, and I forthwith sat down and wrote it in English, reading aloud each evening what I had done during the day to a friend as familiar as I was with the lonely lives in half-deserted New England villages, before the coming of the motor and the telephone."

She insists on her familiarity with New England villages, devoting all the rest of the article to it. And this too is defensive. For the whole truth about the villagers portrayed in her book is that they are "literary." They are a version of village life by the great lady of a Lenox manor, a kindly and sympa-[**viii/ix**]thetic but completely uncomprehending outsider—a version which is practically indistinguishable from a literary convention that was hardening into cliché when she wrote and has since ossified. Mrs. Wharton's New England was a seasonal landscape through which one drove with Henry James, engaged in those frolicsome conversations that always settled down to an infinitely ramifying parenthesis. Though Mr. James might call the landscape thin, it had charm and familiarity for her, but she became helpless as he when the time came to get out of the carriage and knock at a native's door. He was once strolling near his brother's summer place at Chocorua and lost his way; he was set right, he reported, by a peasant who emerged from a copse with a bundle of faggots on his shoulder—presumably one of the psychologist's neighbors who was taking home some bean poles. Mrs. Wharton was just as unable to come to grips with the inhabitants of her landscape. If you bring Ethan, Mattie, and Zenobia into comparison with the people of Mrs. Freeman, Miss Jewett, or even Mrs. Stowe, you perceive at once that Mrs. Wharton was writing from the outside, by logic and the quintessential patronage of supposition, [**ix/x**] and that she lacked the inner knowledge which enables a novelist to transform his reader's assent to acceptance and participation. Mrs. Freeman would have given these people emotion, Miss Jewett would have given them nervous organization, but with Mrs. Wharton they remain a formal design.

They lack, that is, correspondence with the reality of human life as it exists in the Berkshire towns. What they correspond to is the literary convention of dour New England which was, within a few years after *Ethan Frome* was published in 1911, to develop into a literary credo. We were soon to get the "what air yew cacklin' 'bout" Putnams and Mannons of Mr. Eugene O'Neill's bad-fairy tales; Mr. Waldo Frank's New England, "a community rigid in the purpose of acquisition, intolerant of pause, derisive of the silences of life . . . of ugly housings, futile decorations, buried pleasures," where, Mr. Frank said, neurosis was universal and every farm wife wanted to kill at least herself; the Puritan degeneration which Mr. Van Wyck Brooks denounced so episcopally before his reading led him to investigate it, and which scores of minor novelists obediently reproduced on the basis of Mr. [x/xi] Brooks's reports. Mrs. Wharton must have been appalled when she encountered these later versions, but, though she respected the convention whereas they bitterly hated it, they and she accepted it out of books without consulting the reality it was supposed to represent.

The first defect of the three principal characters, then, is that they are cut to pattern: they are what the convention says in advance they must be. The narrow restraint of their minds, the even more rigid constraint of their emotions, their channelled behavior each in respect to a dominant idea, the pettiness and espionage and malice of the village life that shaped them—all these are from convention. They are not people whose behavior a reader can refer to his own experience, but people solving *x* in a narrative formula. That alone would not condemn them, for much formal fiction is vitalized by authentic feeling and characters have often lived vividly within the limits of a convention. But Mrs. Wharton's personal limitations underscored the primary defect. The professional writer could conceive and articulate a splendid formal scheme for the novel, but the great lady of the Lenox manor could [xi/xii] not endow humble characters with convincing or even credible emotions.

Zenobia's neurotic malice does indeed break through into life, but no one can accept for longer than the immediate necessities of the story the love between Ethan and Mattie. At both superficial and basic levels it is lifeless. Mrs. Wharton tells us that they made the world glow for each other, that they were gay together, that they kissed, that they achieved a supreme moment of rebellion against the circumstances of their lives. But she tells us so by assertion only; she does not weld the reader to the characters by the shared emotion that makes fiction live. No kiss in literature has a lower potential than the one at Varnum's gate: it is of the page only, of the developing story, not of the heart. She says that it caps a series of shared incidents, and challenges the imminent separation; but she only says so, she does not move the reader to belief. Similarly with the attempt at suicide and the bitter years that follow it: they are the resolution and coda of a composition, the immensely skillful completion of a design, but hardly a tragedy that, when it occurs to these two, seals the belief of the reader. [xii/xiii]

One accepts the design as story; but when, the story finished, one examines the base in experience, disbelief follows necessarily. Just why were these two so helpless? What weakness or assent in Ethan made the environment so immutable? From what sources does Mattie's meekness flow? If they could be finally moved to rebel against circumstance, what was there to prevent their rebellion from going farther? If love could rouse their will to die, exactly what prevented it from rousing their will to live? What is *necessary* in their lives, their love and rebellion, their attempt at suicide? At its best fiction must have necessity but this novel has none. The answers to such questions must be sought deeper in character than Mrs. Wharton was able to go. Once you have asked the questions you perceive that she could not answer them, and they constitute a judgment.

In place of necessity, Mrs. Wharton is content with circumstance: she does not, as some critics have suggested, imply that the moral law which Ethan and Mattie are trying to violate defeats their attempt at suicide. She was more adult than that! Mr. O'Neill, we may be sure, would have let them con-[**xiii/xiv**]summate their love and then would have overwhelmed them with guilt in denial of the life-force. In the end, Mattie would have crawled from the shattered sled to strangle her illegitimate child, Ethan would have slept for a while with the cows, and Zenobia would have poisoned both of them—all on behalf of some earth-energy to be comprehended only in dithyrambs. But Mrs. Wharton had no thesis: she was practicing detachment. We are not dissenting from a thesis when we confess that the characters make no engagement with us—we are merely stating her limitations. We are saying that they do not "come to life," that what happens to them does not deeply move us. Workmanship has done all that it can do; but workmanship alone has never created life in fiction. Who ever cared what happened to Emma Bovary?

The question is suggestive. Mrs. Wharton's discipleship to Henry James was modified by theories of fiction that sprang up in the wake of Flaubert's *bourgeoise* and came, toward the end of the century, to dominate the writing of fiction. *Ethan Frome* is a *roman d'affaire*. Granted a dreary, repressive, poverty-bound, provincial environment; [**xiv/xv**] granted the circumstance of a sudden affection which might quicken the personalities of two people caught in such an environment; then would it not be ironical to let the impulse which was intended to free them forever miscarry instead and deliver them into more agonizing subjection? In such ways novels were presenting themselves to artists at that time, as ideas whose implications must be worked out completely. One may guess that Mrs. Wharton kindled to her novel as idea since she was incapable of kindling toward it as experience. This was to be *l'affaire Frome,* and the job of the artist was to unravel its circumstances, reveal its pattern, and work out

its *renversement*. That she superbly accomplished just that job explains the longevity of *Ethan Frome*.

There is a difference between the art and the artisanship of fiction, but it is a difference exceedingly difficult to reveal, for the expert workman who is a defective artist is far less common than the potentially fine artist who is a bad workman—and one can never be sure about potentialities. It shows most clearly in such books as this, where a fine novelist who is an expert workman is employed on [**xv/xvi**] material not properly accommodated to her experience and understanding. The book makes plain that fine craftsmanship can sometimes triumph over serious inadequacies. For that it does triumph is clear. It is held in higher esteem than any other of Mrs. Wharton's books, and is certain to endure longer, because it is magnificent story-telling. A week after reading it you will no longer believe in *l'affaire Frome,* but you will not put the book down when you are reading it—whether for the first or the tenth time. By flawless workmanship alone a professional writer has persuaded you to accept an essentially contrived story.

All stories are contrived, of course, but the novelette represents the maximum length at which a reader will accept a contrivance which is of logic only and is not resolved in psychology. That fact is the distinguishing characteristic of the form. Told at greater length, at the length usual in novels, the story would have had to face the questions which reveal its psychological insufficiency. Mrs. Wharton would have had to work out in character and events the necessity which this briefer telling enables her to ignore. She would have had to show why the love [**xvi/xvii**] affair moved just so far without moving farther, why things happened in this way rather than in some other way, why only the outcome selected and described was possible. She would have had, that is, to embody the contrivance of her story in developing motives which would satisfy a reader's most searching doubts. But at the novelette length, the reader will accept an unsupported statement of motive; he is willing to cooperate without prejudice in the open contrivance of the plot. If the contrivance be logical in its own terms, that is enough. Thus the successive uses of the tree into which the sled is to be steered, the pickle dish which implements Zenobia's malice, the kiss of two happier lovers, and similar thematic material skillfully handled are enough of themselves to give the story terms of its own.

The result is a model of structure, joinery, polish, and mass, a durable exhibit of absolutely first-rate literary workmanship. Its success is attested by its having displaced books which Mrs. Wharton felt much more deeply, by the continuing interest in it of which this new edition is one more evidence. No one can read it without surrendering to sheer story; [**xvii/xviii**] no writer can read it without admiration of its craft. It will be with us for a long time yet, a remarkable example of literary skill triumphing over deficiencies of experience and sympathy.

[On *Ethan Frome*: Theme and Background]*

BLAKE NEVIUS (1916–   ) is professor of English at the University of California, Los Angeles. He is editor of *Nineteenth-Century Fiction* and author of *Edith Wharton: A Study of Her Fiction* (1953) and *Robert Herrick: The Development of A Novelist* (1962).

. . . .
. . . Although much has been made of this minor classic of our literature as a picture of New England life and a triumph of style and construction, its relation to Mrs. Wharton's more characteristic and important stories has never been clearly established. *Ethan Frome* is not a "sport." It belongs to [117/118] the main tradition of Mrs. Wharton's fiction, and it has a value, independent of its subject and technique, in helping us to define that tradition. Alfred Kazin has linked it to *The House of Mirth* as a demonstration of the spiritual value of failure, but although this is a recurrent theme in Edith Wharton, particularly in the novels she wrote in the 'twenties, and is inescapable in the conclusion of *The House of Mirth,* it is no mean feat, I think, to reconcile it with the episode which forms the narrative framework of *Ethan Frome.* She was by no means convinced of its soundness, and it is possible, as I intend to suggest, that the spectacle of Ethan's prolonged and hopeless defeat, reinforced by the glimpses of his spiritual isolation, his scarred and twisted body, and his querulous, demanding womenfolk, is intended to convey quite the opposite of what Mr. Kazin finds in the story.

The final, lingering note of the story, it seems to me, is one of despair arising from the contemplation of spiritual waste. So emphatic is it that it drowns out the conventional notion of the value of suffering and defeat. Ethan himself sounds it just before his last, abortive effort to escape his destiny:

Other possibilities had been in him, possibilities sacrificed, one by one, to Zeena's narrow-mindedness and ignorance. And what good had come of it? She was a hundred times bitterer and more discontented than when he had married her: the one pleasure left her was to inflict pain on him. All the healthy instincts of self-defense rose up in him against such waste. . . .

And taking Mrs. Wharton's novels as a whole, that note swells into a refrain whose burden, as George Darrow [118/119] in *The Reef* formulates it, is "the monstrousness of useless sacrifices." Here is the ultimate result of that "immersion of the larger in the smaller nature which is one of the mysteries of the moral life." As a theme, the vanity of self-sacrifice is merged repeatedly with the primary theme of the limits of individual responsibility. A realization of "the monstrousness of useless sacrifices" encourages the characters' selfish, passional bent, which is curbed in turn by the puritanical assertion of responsibility. For Ethan as for most of Edith Wharton's protagonists who are confronted by the same alternatives—Ann Eliza Bunner, Newland Archer, Charlotte Lovell, Kate Clephane, Nona Manford, Martin Boyne—the inherited sense of duty is strong enough to conquer, but the victory leaves in its wake the sense of futility which self-

* Blake Nevius, from *Edith Wharton: A Study of Her Fiction* (Berkley and Los Angeles: University of California Press, 1953), pp. 117–124, 127–129. Reprinted by permission of the publishers.

sacrifice entails. Their moral transactions are such as to preclude a satisfactory balancing of accounts.

How and to what degree does the situation in *Ethan Frome* embody this conflict? No element in the characterization of Ethan is more carefully brought out than the suggestion of his useful, even heroic possibilities. He had longed to become an engineer, had acquired some technical training, and is still reading desultorily in the field when the narrator encounters him. This is one aspect of his personality. There is still another which helps explain why Edith Wharton, who was deeply drawn to nature, is predisposed to treat his case with the utmost sympathy: "He had always been more sensitive than people about him to the appeal of natural beauty. His unfinished studies had given form to this sensibility and even in his unhappiest moments field and sky spoke to him with a deep and powerful persuasion." Add to these qualities his superior gifts of kindness, generosity, [119/120] and sociability, and his impressive physical appearance ("Even then he was the most striking figure in Starkfield, though he was but the ruin of a man"), and it is evident that Edith Wharton set about, as Melville did with Ahab, to invest her rather unpromising human material with a tragic dignity.

It is in view of his potentialities that Ethan's marriage to Zeena is a catastrophe. By the time Mattie Silver appears on the scene, he is only twenty-eight but already trapped by circumstances and unable to extend the horizon of his future beyond the family graveyard. Mattie, once she has become the victim of Zeena's jealousy, offers a way out which Ethan is quick to follow. But immediately his plans are set afoot, things begin to close in on him again: farm and mill are mortgaged, he has no credit, and time is against him. Moreover, even in the heat of his resentment he cannot disregard Zeena's plight: "It was only by incessant labour and personal supervision that Ethan drew a meagre living from the land, and his wife, even if she were in better health than she imagined, could never carry such a burden alone." His rebellion dies out, but only to be rekindled the next morning as Mattie is about to leave. Suddenly it occurs to him that if he pleads Zeena's illness and the need of a servant, Andrew Hale may give him an advance on some lumber. He starts on foot for Starkfield, meets Mrs. Hale en route, is touched by her expression of sympathy ("You've had an awful mean time, Ethan Frome"), continues toward his rendezvous—and is suddenly pulled up short by the realization that he is planning to appeal to the Hales' sympathy to obtain money from them on false pretenses. It is the turning point of the action: [120/121]

> With the sudden perception of the point to which his madness had carried him, the madness fell and he saw his life before him as it was. He was a poor man, the husband of a sickly woman, whom his desertion would leave alone and destitute; and even if he had the heart to desert her he could have done so only by deceiving two kindly people who had pitied him.

Although he is neatly hemmed in by circumstances, it is Ethan's own sense of responsibility that blocks the last avenue of escape and condemns him to a life of sterile expiation.

In *Ethan Frome* all the themes I have mentioned are developed without the complexity that the more sophisticated characters and setting of *The Fruit of the Tree* and (as we shall see) *The Reef* require; they are reduced to the barest statement of their possibilities. To a person of Ethan's limited experience and his capacity for straightforward judgments, the issues present themselves with the least ambiguity or encouragement to evasion; and in this, I believe, we have the measure of the subject's value for Mrs. Wharton. As her characters approach her own sphere, their motives are disentangled with increasing difficulty from her own, and their actions are regulated by a closer censure; they become more complex and are apt to lose their way amid fine distinctions and tentative judgments. They are aware, like Woburn in the short story "A Cup of Cold Water," of the impossibility of basing a decision upon absolutes:

Was not all morality based on a convention? What was the stanchest code of ethics but a trunk with a series of false bottoms? Now and then one had the illusion of getting down [121/122] to absolute right or wrong, but it was only a false bottom—a removable hypothesis—with another false bottom underneath. There was no getting beyond the relative.

Ethan Frome is closer than any of her other characters to the source of the ideas that underlie Edith Wharton's ethical judgments. Puritanism has lost very little of its hold on that portion of the New England mind which he represents and its ideas have not been weakened, as they have in the more populous industrial and commercial centers, by two centuries of enlightenment based on what Bernard Shaw called the Mercanto-Christian doctrine of morality. It is not surprising that many persons unacquainted with Edith Wharton's biography associate her —and not wholly on the strength of *Ethan Frome*—with Boston or with New England as a whole. Whatever the influences exerted by her New York origin and background and her long career abroad, it is the moral order of Ethan Frome's world that governs the view of reality in all her novels.

For this reason, and for others I will suggest, I am unable to appreciate John Crowe Ransom's objections to Mrs. Wharton's handling of point of view in *Ethan Frome,* a problem he assumes to have bothered her more than I suspect it really did.[6] In trying to reconstruct her approach to a solution, he writes that "if Ethan should tell it himself, it would not be identifiable with the main body of Mrs. Wharton's fiction." I am not sure why it is absolutely desirable that it *should* be, but, at any rate, the difficulty does not seem to have bothered the author of either "Bunner Sisters" or *Sum-*

mer, which are no more readily identifiable than *Ethan Frome* with her usual subjects. "But if she should tell it," Ransom continues, [122/123] "it would very likely be the story of a rather metamorphosed Ethan." Her "trained and sophisticated sensibility . . . would have falsified the whole." To this last suggestion, one can only reply that it would have in any case, whatever point of view she might have chosen. Nevertheless, Ransom concludes that she "temporized": "She invented a special reporter for Ethan in the person of a young man of sensibility and education very like her own. In theory it gained for her this, that the reporter became a man; and this, that not being herself he need not render quite the complete spiritual history of events associated with her name as an author. In effect, it gained her very little."

This is raising difficulties where they do not necessarily exist. In the first place, Edith Wharton was simply following the structural method of Balzac's "La Grand Bretèche," as her hint in the preface and a comparison of the stories will confirm. She did not apply it with Balzac's success, however, for, as Ransom has correctly noted, her narrator's "vision" of Ethan's story (not "version," as Ransom misquotes) is based in large part on data that we cannot imagine any of the principals supplying, so that the story *is* in reality a "vision" rather than a "version." In the second place, the narrators employed in the framework of Edith Wharton's early stories are *always* men— whether because she had, as her contemporaries claimed, a masculine mind or because this refinement of the point of view allowed her greater freedom, I am not sure. But the choice is particularly defensible in *Ethan Frome,* first, because the narrator must have a pretext for visiting Starkfield, and this is more easily supplied for an engineer than for a woman with the requisite "sensibility and education," and second, [123/124]

6 "Characters and Character," *American Review,* VI (Jan., 1936), 271–288.

because there must be some probability established for Ethan's inviting the narrator into his home—over and above, that is, the accident of the storm. Finally, I am not so willing to assume, as Ransom and many others have, that ten years' residence in the Berkshires (even allowing for the annual jaunts to Europe) was not enough to give Mrs. Wharton the needed understanding of the lives of her poorer neighbors. "When the mind is imaginative," writes Henry James in "The Art of Fiction," ". . . it takes to itself the faintest hints of life, it converts the very pulses of the air into revelations." In *The Valley of Decision* Edith Wharton had already demonstrated that she could do this with the materials of history. Why not, then, with the life just beyond her doorstep? . . . [**124/127**]

. . . *Ethan Frome* marks a gain in artistry that was to be consolidated later in *The Reef* and *The Age of Innocence.* The first important work to appear after Edith Wharton had established her permanent residence abroad, it had been undertaken as an exercise in French to modernize her idioms, but had been abandoned after a few weeks. A sojourn at the Mount, some years later, had revived the story in her mind, and it had been written in Paris during the following winter. From the directness and simplicity of the style of the final version, one might suppose that it had been composed entirely in French and then translated, but it was in fact an independent growth from the original seed. She and Walter Berry had "talked the tale over page by page," and the results of their collaboration may be glimpsed in the fragment of a working version preserved among the manuscripts at Yale. Berry was a rigorous taskmaster. "With each book," Edith Wharton acknowledged gratefully, "he exacted a higher standard in economy of expression, in purity of language, in the avoidance of the hackneyed and precious." The stylistic restraint of the final version, unusual even

for Mrs. Wharton, may in part be a tribute to his discipline. How many revisions the tale underwent [**127/128**] may never be known, but a comparison of the manuscript fragment with the corresponding portion of the printed text indicates that Edith Wharton worked hard to meet Berry's standards and to eliminate redundancies, circumlocutions, and ambiguous or misleading expressions, realizing that the language as well as the theme of *Ethan Frome* had to be treated "starkly and summarily.". . .

Enough has been said, by Mrs. Wharton among others, about the technical resourcefulness brought into play by the peculiar difficulties of telling Ethan's story; but in view of the widespread feeling that the author's human sympathies were hobbled by her rationalism, it should be stressed that the best touches in the story are there because she felt her subject deeply enough to be able to charge it with conviction at every point. The details are few but impressive; they arise directly and easily, and always with the sharpest pertinence, from the significant grounds of character and situation; they are, as Percy Lubbock suggests, "the natural and sufficient channels of great emotion." [2] Every reader will recall some of them: Mattie's tribute to the winter sunset—"It looks just as if it was painted"; Ethan's reluctance to have Mattie see him follow Zeena into their bedroom; the removal of Mattie's trunk; the watchful, sinister presence of Zeena's cat disturbing the intimacy of the lovers' evening together by appropriating her mistress' place at the table, breaking the pickle dish, and later setting Zeena's rocking chair in motion. Zeena may not be a sympathetic character, but there is a moment when she makes us forget everything but her wronged humanity. As she confronts the guilty lovers, holding the fragments of her [**128/129**] beloved pickle dish, her face streaming with tears, we have a sudden and terrible glimpse of the starved emotional life that has made her

---

[2] "The Novels of Edith Wharton," 184.

what she is. The novelist's compassion can reach no further.

Although it functioned generally at a mundane level, Edith Wharton's imagination could occasionally be roused to symbol-making activity by the conjunction of a theme and a setting both deeply cherished and understood. In *Ethan Frome* her theme is enhanced by every feature of the landscape: by the "orchard of starved appletrees writhing over a hillside among outcroppings of slate," the crazily slanted headstones in the Frome graveyard, the truncated "L" of Ethan's farmhouse in which one saw "the image of his own shrunken body," but predominantly by the landscape as a whole, buried under snow, silent and incommunicative as the characters. The method looks ahead to *Summer,* with its naturalistic symbol of the Mountain and its subtle accommodation of the human drama to the rhythm of the changing seasons; to the moment in *The Reef* when Darrow recalls his vision of Anna Summers advancing toward him slowly down an avenue of trees, now transformed in his imagination to the passing years, with the "light and shade of old memories and new hopes playing variously on her"; and to *Hudson River Bracketed,* with its dominating symbol of the Willows, equated in Vance Weston's mind with the Past he is struggling to recapture in his first novel. Only in *Ethan Frome,* however, is the symbolism sustained by every element in the setting. It is the one occasion in her longer fiction when her imagination worked freely and without faltering in this extra dimension. . . .

The Morality of Inertia*

LIONEL TRILLING (1905–   ), teacher, literary critic, and occasional novelist and short-story writer, is one of this country's most versatile and respected men of letters. He is George Edward Woodberry Professor of Literature and Criticism at Columbia University, where he has taught since 1932, and the author of *Matthew Arnold* (1939), *E. M. Forster* (1943), *The Middle of the Journey* (a novel; 1947), and three notable volumes of essays, *The Liberal Imagination* (1950), *The Opposing Self* (1955), and *Beyond Culture* (1965).

When The Institute for Religious and Social Studies of The Jewish Theological Seminary of America planned a series of lectures on "Literary Presentations of Great Moral Issues" and asked me to give one of the talks, I was disposed to accept the invitation, for I have a weakness for the general subject. But I hesitated over the particular instance, for I was asked to discuss the moral issues in *Ethan Frome*. I had not read Edith Wharton's little novel in a good many years, but I remembered it with no pleasure or admiration. I recalled it as not at all the sort of book that deserved to stand in a list which included *The Brothers Karamazov* and *Billy Budd, Foretopman*. If it presented a moral issue at all, I could not bring to mind what that issue was. And so I postponed my acceptance of the invitation and made it conditional upon my being able to come to terms with the subject assigned to me.

Ethan Frome, when I read it again, turned out to be pretty much as I had recalled it. It isn't a great book, or even a fine book. It seemed to me a factitious book, perhaps even a cruel book. I was puzzled to understand how it ever came to be put on the list, why anyone should want to have it discussed as an example of moral perception. Then I remembered

its reputation, which, in America, is very considerable. It is sometimes spoken of as an American classic. Every literate person has read it. It is often assigned to high school and college students as a text for study.

But the high and solemn repute in which it stands is, I am sure, in [**37/38**] large part a mere accident of American culture. *Ethan Frome* appeared in 1911, at a time when, to a degree that we can now only wonder at, American literature was committed to optimism, cheerfulness, and gentility. What William Dean Howells called "the smiling aspects of life" had an importance in the literature of America some fifty years ago which is unmatched in the literature of any other time and place. It was inevitable that those who were critical of the prevailing culture and who wished to foster in America a higher and more serious literature should put a heavy stress upon the grimmer aspects of life, that they should equate the smiling aspects with falsehood, the grimmer aspects with truth. For these devoted people, sickened as they were by cheerfulness and hope, the word "stark" seemed to carry the highest possible praise a critical review or a blurb could bestow, with "relentless" and "inevitable" as its proper variants. *Ethan Frome*

* Lionel Trilling, "The Morality of Inertia," in *Great Moral Dilemmas*, edited by Robert M. MacIver (New York: Harper & Brothers, 1956), pp. 37–46. Reprinted in Lionel Trilling, *A Gathering of Fugitives* (Boston: Beacon Press, 1956). Used by permission of the Beacon Press. Copyright © 1955, 1956 by Lionel Trilling.

101

was admired because it was stark—its action, we note, takes place in the New England village of Starkville—and because the fate it describes is *relentless* and *inevitable*.

No one would wish to question any high valuation that may be given to the literary representation of unhappy events—except, perhaps, as the high valuation may be a mere cliché of an intellectual class, except as it is supposed to seem the hallmark of the superior sensibility and intelligence of that class. Then we have the right, and the duty, to look sniffishly at starkness, and relentlessness and inevitability, to cock a skeptical eye at grimness. And I am quite unable to overcome my belief that *Ethan Frome* enjoys its high reputation because it satisfies the modern snobbishness about tragedy and pain.

We can never speak of Edith Wharton without some degree of respect. She brought to her novels a strong if limited intelligence, and notable powers of observation, and a genuine desire to tell the truth, a desire which in some parts she satisfied. But she was a woman in whom we cannot fail to see a limitation of heart, and this limitation makes itself manifest as a literary and moral deficiency of her work, and of *Ethan Frome* especially. It appears in the deadness of her prose, and more flagrantly in the suffering of her characters. When the characters of a story suffer, they do so at the behest of [38/39] their author—the author is responsible for their suffering and must justify his cruelty by the seriousness of his moral intention. The author of *Ethan Frome*, it seemed to me, could not lay claim to any such justification. Her intention in writing the story was not adequate to the dreadful fate she contrives for her characters. She but indulges herself by what she contrives—she is, as the phrase goes, "merely literary." This is not to say that the merely literary intention does not make its very considerable effects. There is in *Ethan Frome* an image of life-in-death, of hell-on-earth,

which is not easily to be forgotten: the crippled Ethan, and Zeena, his dreadful wife, and Mattie, the once charming girl he had loved, now bedridden and querulous with pain, all living out their death in the kitchen of the desolate Frome farm—a perpetuity of suffering memorializes a moment of passion. It is terrible to contemplate, it is unforgettable, but the mind can do nothing with it, can only endure it.

My new reading of the book, then, did not lead me to suppose that it justified its reputation, but only confirmed my recollection that *Ethan Frome* was a dead book, the product of mere will, of the cold hard literary will. What is more, it seemed to me quite unavailable to any moral discourse. In the context of morality, there is nothing to say about *Ethan Frome*. It presents no moral issue at all.

For consider the story it tells. A young man of good and gentle character is the only son of a New England farm couple. He has some intellectual gifts and some desire to know the world, and for a year he is happy attending a technical school in a nearby city. But his father is incapacitated by a farm accident, and Ethan dutifully returns to manage the failing farm and sawmill. His father dies; his mother loses her mental faculties, and during her last illness she is nursed by a female relative whom young Ethan marries, for no reason other than that he is bemused by loneliness. The new wife immediately becomes a shrew, a harridan, and a valetudinarian—she lives only to be ill. Because Zeena now must spare herself, the Fromes take into their home a gentle and charming young girl, a destitute cousin of the wife. Ethan and Mattie fall in love, innocently but deeply. The wife, perceiving this, plans to send the girl away, her place to be taken by a hired servant whose wages the husband cannot [39/40] possibly afford. In despair at their separation Mattie and Ethan attempt suicide. They mean to die by sledding down a steep hill and crashing into a great elm at the bottom. Their plan fails: both survive the crash, Ethan to be sorely crippled, Mattie to be bedridden in perpetual pain. Now the wife Zeena surrenders her claim to a mysterious pathology and becomes the devoted nurse and jailer of the lovers. The terrible tableau to which I have referred is ready for our inspection.

It seemed to me that it was quite impossible to talk about this story. This is not to say that the story is without interest as a story, but what interest it may have does not yield discourse, or at least not moral discourse.

But as I began to explain why I could not accept the invitation to lecture about the book, it suddenly came over me how very strange a phenomenon the book made—how remarkable it was that a story should place before us the dreadful image of three ruined and tortured lives, showing how their ruin came about, and yet propose no moral issue of any kind. And if *issue* seems to imply something more precisely formulated than we have a right to demand of a story, then it seemed to me no less remarkable that the book had scarcely any moral reverberation, that strange and often beautiful sound we seem to hear generated in the air by a tale of suffering, a sound which is not always music, which does not always have a "meaning," but which yet entrances us, like the random notes of an Aeolian harp, or merely the sound of the wind in the chimney. The moral sound that *Ethan Frome* makes is a dull thud. And this seemed to me so remarkable, indeed, that, in the very act of saying why I could not possibly discuss *Ethan Frome,* I found the reason why it must be discussed.

It is, as I have suggested, a very great fault in *Ethan Frome* that it presents no moral issue, and no moral reverberation. A certain propriety controls the literary representation of human suffering. This propriety dictates that the representation of pain may not be, as it were, gratuitous; it must not be an end in itself. The naked act of representing, or contemplat-

ing, human suffering is a self-indulgence, and it may be a cruelty. Between a tragedy and a spectacle in the [**40/41**] Roman circus there is at least this much similarity, that the pleasure both afford derives from observing the pain of others. A tragedy is always on the verge of cruelty. What saves it from the actuality of cruelty is that it has an intention beyond itself. This intention may be so simple a one as that of getting us to do something practical about the cause of the suffering or to help actual sufferers, or at least to feel that we should; or it may lead us to look beyond apparent causes to those which the author wishes us to think of as more real, such as Fate, or the will of the gods, or the will of God; or it may challenge our fortitude or intelligence or piety.

A sense of the necessity of some such intention animates all considerations of the strange paradox of tragedy. Aristotle is concerned to solve the riddle of how the contemplation of human suffering can possibly be pleasurable, of why its pleasure is permissible. He wanted to know what literary conditions were needed to keep a tragedy from being a mere display of horror. Here it is well to remember that the Greeks were not so concerned as we have been led to believe to keep all dreadful things off the stage—in the presentation of Aristotle's favorite tragedy, the audience saw Jocasta hanging from a beam, it saw the representation of Oedipus's bloody sightless eyesockets. And so Aristotle discovered, or pretended to discover, that tragedy did certain things to protect itself from being merely cruel. It chose, Aristotle said, a certain kind of hero; he was of a certain social and moral stature; he had a certain degree of possibility of free choice, or at least the appearance or illusion of free choice; he must justify his fate, or seem to justify it, by his moral condition, being neither wholly good nor wholly bad, having a particular fault that collaborates with destiny to bring about his ruin. The purpose of all these specifications for the tragic hero is to assure us that we witness something more than mere passivity when we witness the hero's suffering, that we witness something more than suffering, that the suffering has, as we say, some meaning, some show of rationality.

Aristotle's theory of tragedy has had its way with the world to an extent which is perhaps out of proportion to its comprehensiveness and accuracy. Its success is largely due to its having dealt so openly [**41/42**] with the paradox of tragedy. It serves to explain away any guilty feelings that we may have at deriving pleasure from suffering.

But at the same time that the world has accepted Aristotle's theory of tragedy, it has also been a little uneasy about some of its implications. The element of the theory that causes uneasiness in modern times is the matter of the stature of the hero. To a society touched by egalitarian sentiments, the requirement that the hero be a man of rank seems to deny the presumed dignity of tragedy to men of lesser status. And to a culture which questions the freedom of the will, Aristotle's hero seems to be a little beside the point. Aristotle's prescription for the tragic hero is clearly connected with his definition, in his *Ethics,* of the nature of an ethical action. He tells us that a truly ethical action must be a free choice between two alternatives. This definition is then wonderfully complicated by a further requirement—that the moral man must be so trained in making the right choice that he makes it as a matter of habit, makes it, as it were, instinctively. Yet it *is* a choice, and reason plays a part in its making. But we, of course, don't give to reason the same place in the moral life that Aristotle gave it. And in general, over the past hundred and fifty years, dramatists and novelists have tried their hand at the representation of human suffering without the particular safeguards against cruelty which Aristotle perceived, or contrived. A very large part of the literature of Western Europe may

be understood in terms of an attempt to invert or criticize the heroic prescription of the hero, by burlesque and comedy, or by the insistence on the commonplace, the lowering of the hero's social status and the diminution of his power of reasoned choice. The work of Fielding may serve as a sufficient example of how the mind of Europe has been haunted by the great images and great prescriptions of classical tragedy, and how it has tried to lay that famous ghost. When Fielding calls his hero Tom Jones, he means that his young man is not Orestes or Achilles; when he calls him a foundling, he is suggesting that Tom Jones is not, all appearances to the contrary notwithstanding, Oedipus.

Edith Wharton was following where others led. Her impulse in conceiving the story of Ethan Frome was not, however, that of moral experimentation. It was, as I have said, a purely literary impulse, in [**42/43**] the bad sense of the word literary. Her aim is not that of Wordsworth in any of his stories of the suffering poor, to require it of us that we open our minds to realization of the kinds of people whom suffering touches. Nor is it that of Flaubert in *Madame Bovary,* to wring from sordid circumstances all the pity and terror of an ancient tragic fable. Nor is it that of Dickens or Zola, to shake us with the perception of social injustice, to instruct us in the true nature of social life and to dispose us to indignant opinion and action. These are not essentially literary intentions; they are moral intentions. But all that Edith Wharton has in mind is to achieve that grim tableau of which I have spoken, of pain and imprisonment, of life-in-death. About the events that lead up to this tableau, there is nothing she finds to say, nothing whatever. The best we can say about the meaning of the story is that it might perhaps be a subject of discourse in the context of rural sociology—it might be understood to exemplify the thesis that love and joy do not flourish on povertystricken New England farms. If we try to bring it into the context of morality, its meaning is limited to mere cultural considerations—that is, to people who like their literature to show the "smiling aspects of life," it may be thought to say, "This is the aspect that life really has, as grim as this"; while to people who repudiate a literature that represents only the smiling aspects of life it says, "How intelligent and how brave you are to be able to understand that life is as grim as this." It is really not very much to say.

And yet there is in *Ethan Frome* an idea of very considerable importance. It is there by reason of the author's deficiencies, not by reason of her powers—it is there because it suits Edith Wharton's rather dull literary intention to be content with telling a story about people who do not make moral decisions, whose fate cannot have moral reverberations. The idea is this: that moral inertia, the *not* making of moral decisions, constitutes a very large part of the moral life of humanity.

This isn't an idea that literature likes to deal with. Literature is charmed by energy and dislikes inertia. It characteristically represents morality as positive action. The same is true of the moral philosophy of the West—has been true ever since Aristotle defined a truly moral [43/ 44] act by its energy of reason, of choice. A later development of this tendency said that an act was really moral only if it went against the inclination of the person performing the act: the idea was parodied as saying that one could not possibly act morally to one's friends, only to one's enemies.

Yet the dull daily world sees something below this delightful preoccupation of literature and moral philosophy. It is aware of the morality of inertia, and of its function as a social base, as a social cement. It knows that duties are done for no other reason than that they are said to be duties; for no other reason, sometimes, than that the doer has not really been able to conceive of any other course, has, perhaps, been afraid to think of any oth-

er course. Hobbes said of the Capitol geese that saved Rome by their cackling that they were the salvation of the city, not because they were they but there. How often the moral act is performed not because we are we but because we are there! This is the morality of habit, or the morality of biology. This is Ethan Frome's morality, simple, unquestioning, passive, even masochistic. His duties as a son are discharged because he is a son; his duties as a husband are discharged because he is a husband. He does nothing because he is a moral man. At one point in his story he is brought to moral crisis —he must choose between his habituated duty to his wife and his duty and inclination to the girl he loves. It is quite impossible for him to deal with the dilemma in the high way that literature and moral philosophy prescribe, by reason and choice. Choice is incompatible with his idea of his existence; he can only elect to die.

Literature, of course, is not wholly indifferent to what I have called the morality of habit and biology, the morality of inertia. But literature, when it deals with this morality, is tempted to qualify its dulness by endowing it with a certain high grace. There is never any real moral choice for the Felicité of Flaubert's story, "A Simple Heart." She is all pious habit of virtue, and of blind, unthinking, unquestioning love. There are, of course, actually such people as Felicité, simple, good, loving—quite stupid in their love, not choosing where to bestow it. We meet such people frequently in literature, in the pages of Balzac, Dickens, Dostoievsky, Joyce, Faulkner, Hemingway. [44/45] They are of a quite different order of being from those who try the world with their passion and their reason; they are by way of being saints, of the less complicated kind. They do not really exemplify what I mean by the morality of inertia or of biology. Literature is uncomfortable in the representation of the morality of inertia or of biology, and overcomes its discomfort by representing it with the added grace of that extravagance which we denominate saintliness.

But the morality of inertia is to be found in precise exemplification in one of Wordsworth's poems. Wordsworth is preeminent among the writers who experimented in the representation of new kinds and bases of moral action—he has a genius for imputing moral existence to people who, according to the classical morality, should have no life at all. And he has the coldness to make this imputation without at the same time imputing the special grace and interest of saintliness. The poem I have in mind is ostensibly about a flower, but the transition from the symbol to the human fact is clearly, if awkwardly, made. The flower is a small celandine, and the poet observes that it has not, in the natural way of flowers, folded itself against rough weather:

But lately, one rough day, this Flower I passed
And recognized it, though in altered form,
Now standing as an offering to the blast,
And buffeted at will by rain and storm.

I stopped, and said with inly-muttered voice,
It doth not love the shower nor seek the cold;
This neither is its courage nor its choice,
But its necessity in being old.

Neither courage nor choice, but necessity: it cannot do otherwise. Yet it acts as if by courage and choice. This is the morality imposed by brute circumstance, by biology, by habit, by the unspoken social demand which we have not the strength to refuse, or, often, to imagine refusing. People are scarcely ever praised for living according to this morality—we do not suppose it to be a morality at all until we see it being broken.

This is morality as it is conceived by the great mass of people in [45/46] the world. And with this conception of morality goes the almost entire negation of any connection between morality and destiny. A superstitious belief in retribution may play its part in the thought of simple people, but essentially they think of catastrophes as fortuitous, without explanation, without reason. They live in the moral universe of the *Book of Job*. In complex lives, morality does in some part determine destiny; in most lives it does not. Between the moral life of Ethan and Mattie and their terrible fate we cannot make any reasonable connection. Only a moral judgment cruel to the point of insanity could speak of it as anything but accidental.

I have not spoken of the morality of inertia in order to praise it but only in order to recognize it, to suggest that when we keep our minds fixed on what the great invigorating books tell us about the moral life, we obscure the large bulking dull mass of moral fact. Morality is not only the high, torturing, brilliant dilemmas of Ivan Karamazov and Captain Vere. It is also the deeds performed without thought, without choice, perhaps even without love, as Zeena Frome ministers to Ethan and Mattie. The morality of inertia, of the dull, unthinking round of daily duties, may, and often does, yield the immorality of inertia; the example that will most readily occur to us is that of the good simple people, so true to their family responsibilities, who gave no thought to the concentration camps in whose shadow they lived. No: the morality of inertia is not to be praised, but it must be recognized. And Edith Wharton's little novel is not to be praised, but it must be recognized for bringing to our attention what we, and literature, so easily forget.

Imagery and Symbolism in *Ethan Frome**

KENNETH BERNARD (1930–   ) is an associate professor of English at Long Island University. He has published widely in American journals, both poetry and fiction as well as criticism. In recent years he has written several articles on the American novelist Charles Brockden Brown.

". . . I had an uneasy sense that the New England of fiction bore little—except a vague botanical and dialectical—resemblance to the harsh and beautiful land as I had seen it. Even the abundant enumeration of sweet-fern, asters and mountain-laurel, and the conscientious reproduction of the vernacular, left me with the feeling that the outcropping granite had in both cases been overlooked."

Edith Wharton, Introduction, *Ethan Frome*

A common criticism of Edith Wharton's *Ethan Frome* is that it is too contrived. In the last analysis, the characters seem peculiarly unmotivated, put through their paces in a clever, but mechanical, way. Such an opinion can only be the result of a cursory reading. It is true that the book has a kind of stylistic and organizational brilliance. But it is not merely a display; it is invariably at the service of plot and character. The nature of her subject imposed certain difficulties on Wharton, particularly her characters' lack of articulation. How could she, without over-narrating, get at a deep problem involving such characters when they do not speak enough to reveal that problem? Frome's [178/179] character and his marital relationship are at the heart of the novel, but they are revealed only indirectly. Wharton solved her difficulty in a masterful way by her use of imagery and symbolism. It is in her use of imagery and symbolism that the depths of the story are to be found. Without an understanding of them, a reader *would* find the characters unmotivated and the tragedy contrived. For easy discussion, the imagery and symbolism may be divided into three parts: the compatibility of setting and character, the uses of light and dark, and the sexual symbolism. A survey of these three parts in the novel will, it is hoped, clarify the real story in *Ethan Frome* by adding a new dimension of meaning.

I

The beginning of this new dimension of meaning is the first mention of the New England village—Starkfield. On many levels the *locus* of the story is a stark field. The village lies under "a sky of iron," points of the dipper over it hang "like icicles," and Orion flashes "cold fires." The countryside is "gray and lonely." Each farmhouse is "mute and cold as a grave-stone." This characterization of Starkfield is consistent throughout the book. Frome, in all ways, fits into this setting. On several occasions his integration with it is described. The narrator, upon first seeing him, sees him as "bleak and unapproachable." Later he says of Frome, "He seemed a part of the mute melancholy landscape, an incarnation of its frozen woe, with all that was warm and sentient in him bound fast below the surface . . . he lived in a depth of moral isolation too remote for casual access."

* Kenneth Bernard, "Imagery and Symbolism in *Ethan Frome*," *College English*, XXIII (December 1961), 178–184. Reprinted with the permission of the National Council of Teachers of English and Kenneth Bernard.

Frome, unhappily married to Zeena, and pining for her cousin Mattie, is indeed parallel to the Starkfield setting. Everything on the surface is hard and frozen. His feeling, his love, for Mattie cannot break loose, just as spring and summer are fast bound by winter's cold. Mattie, appropriately, has the effect of loosening the rigid physical and emotional landscape. At one point, when she speaks, "The iron heavens seemed to melt down sweetness." Again, she is "like the lighting of a fire on a cold hearth." Frome, however, who has suffered "the profound accumulated cold of many Starkfield winters," does not thaw easily. He remembers when his feelings were free, or, as he puts it, when he was once in Florida, climatically (and emotionally) the opposite of Starkfield: "Yes: I was down there once, and for a good while afterward I could call up the sight of it in winter. But now it's all snowed under." Finally there is Frome's inarticulateness. Not only are his feelings locked, frozen; his very speech is also, beyond the natural reticence of the local people. Neither he nor the landscape can express its warm and tender part. When Mattie once pleases him immensely, he gropes "for a dazzling phrase," but is able to utter only a "growl of rapture: 'Come along.'" Later he is again thrilled by her: "Again he struggled for the all expressive word, and again, his arm in hers, found only a deep 'Come along.'" He is truly a man of "dumb melancholy."

The separation of feeling from its expression, the idea of emotion being locked away, separated, or frozen, just as Starkfield is bound by ice and snow, is demonstrated also by the Frome farm. The house seems to "shiver in the wind," has a "broken down gate," and has an "unusually forlorn and stunted look." More important, though, is the "L." Wharton gives a full description of the New England farm "L":

that long deep-roofed adjunct usually built at right angles to the main house, and connecting it,

by way of storerooms and tool-house, with the woodshed and cow-barn. Whether because of its symbolic sense, the image it presents of a life linked with the soil, and [179/180] enclosing in itself the chief sources of warmth and nourishment, or whether merely because of the consolatory thought that it enables the dwellers in that harsh climate to get to their morning's work without facing the weather, it is certain that the "L" rather than the house itself seems to be the center, the actual hearth-stone of the New England farm.

Frome casually mentions to the narrator that he had had to take down the "L." Thus Frome's home is disjointed, separated from its vital functions, even as he is. The narrator, not unnaturally, sees in Frome's words about the "diminished dwelling the image of his own shrunken body." Just as Frome is emotionally trapped, just as Starkfield is frozen in the winter landscape, just as Frome's home is cut off from its vitals, so too is he cut off physically from his former strength, trapped in his crippled frame. Images of being caught, bound, trapped are frequent. "He was a prisoner for life." "It seemed to Ethan that his heart was bound with cords which an unseen hand was tightening with every tick of the clock." "I'm tied hand and foot, Matt." Although Mattie is described with flight images like "the flit of a bird in branches," and birds making "short perpendicular flights," the last such image describing her is of her lashes beating like "netted butterflies," and her last "twittering" is her pitiful cry after the unsuccessful suicide attempt, when she is a broken, pain-racked body. Even Mattie, Frome's one hope of escape, is trapped. On top of this, Frome mentions that before the railroad came to a nearby town the road by his farm was a main route, implying that business was better: "We're kinder side-tracked here now." The farm, too, is separated from its former economic vitality. Thus the setting of the novel, the landscape and the farm, is parallel to Frome's condition and serves to illuminate it. But Wharton does not stop at this point.

II

There is hardly a page throughout the book that does not have some reference to light and dark. Wharton uses all of them with effect. The supreme light image is Mattie Silver, as her name implies. She is in contrast to everything in Starkfield; her feelings bubble near the surface. Frome, on the other hand, is all dark. He lives in the dark, especially emotionally. At the beginning of the novel, when he has come to meet Mattie, she is dancing gaily in a church filled with "broad bands of yellow light." Frome keeps "out of the range of the revealing rays from within." "Hugging the shadow," he stands in the "frosty darkness" and looks in. Later he catches up to her "in the black shade of the Varnum spruces," the spot from where they finally begin the attempted suicide that cripples them. He stands with her in "the gloom of the spruces," where it is "so dark . . . he could barely see the shape of her head," or walks with her "in silence through the blackness of the hemlock-shaded lane." Blackness is his element. As they walk back to the farm he revels in their closeness. "It was during their night walks back to the farm that he felt most intensely the sweetness of this communion." Their love is a bloom of night. "He would have liked to stand there with her all night in the blackness." He does not see Mattie so much as sense her: ". . . he felt, in the darkness, that her face was lifted quickly to his." "They strained their eyes to each other through the icy darkness." Frome's favorite spot is a secluded place in the woods called Shadow Pond. On their last visit there "the darkness descended with them, dropping down like a black veil from the heavy hemlock boughs." Frome cannot seem to get out of the dark. And often, as in quotations above, the dark is pregnant with suggestions of death and cold. Frome's kitchen, on their return from the village, [**180/181**] has "the deadly chill of a vault after the dry cold of night." As Ethan settles in his tomblike house, Mattie's effect on him dies away. He lies in bed and watches the light from her candle, which

> sending its small ray across the landing, drew a scarcely perceptible line of light under his door. He kept his eyes fixed on the light till it vanished. Then the room grew perfectly black, and not a sound was audible but Zeena's asthmatic breathing.

Without Mattie's "light" he is left with the ugly reality of his wife. In numerous small ways also Wharton makes the light and dark images work for her. When Mattie relieves Ethan's jealousy at one point, "The blackness lifted and light flooded Ethan's brain." When Mattie is told by Zeena she must go, and she repeats the words to Ethan, "The words went on sounding between them as though a torch of warning flew from hand to hand through a dark landscape." Before their suicide plunge, "The spruces swathed them in blackness and silence." A bitter argument between Ethan and Zeena is "as senseless and savage as a physical fight between two enemies in the darkness." After, Zeena's face "stood grimly out against the uncurtained pane, which had turned from grey to black." The cumulative effect of all these images is to tell us a great deal about Frome and his tortured psyche.

The most important thing the images of light and dark reveal about Frome is that he is a negative person. Frome is a heroic figure: nothing less than the entire landscape can suffice to describe him effectively; his agony is as broad and deep as that of the winter scene. But he is not tragic because he is a man of great potential subdued and trapped by forces beyond his capacity. His tragedy is entirely of his own making. He is weak. His character never changes. Both before and after the accident he is the same. Like his environment he has a kind of dumb endurance for harsh conditions. There are several indications of his weakness besides his identity with darkness. Frome married Zeena because she had nursed his mother through her final illness. He was twenty-one and she twenty-eight. He married her less because he loved her than because he needed a replacement for his mother. Certainly it is Zeena who cracks the whip in the household, and Ethan who jumps. What Zeena says, goes. Frome "had often thought since that it would not have happened if his mother had died in spring instead of winter . . ." When he and Mattie are about to attempt suicide, Mattie sitting in front of Ethan on the sled, he asks her to change places with him. She asks why. Quite sincerely he answers, "Because I—because I want to feel you holding me." He wants to die being cuddled and comforted, leaving to Mattie the role of protector and shelterer.

Throughout the book, Frome recognizes his futility and accepts it rather than trying to fight his way out of it. He does not ever realistically reach for a solution. His love inspires little more than dreams. He thinks of another man who left his wife for another woman and invests the event with fairy tale qualities: "They had a little girl with fair curls, who wore a gold locket and was dressed like a princess." Once he imagines Zeena might be dead: "What if tramps had been there—what if . . ." When he spends his one night alone with Mattie, instead of thinking of a way to achieve permanence for their relationship he "set his imagination adrift on the fiction that they had always spent their evenings thus and would always go on doing so . . ." Ironically, this is just about what he achieves by crippling instead of killing himself and Mattie. He did not, however, envision that Zeena would be a necessary part of the arrangement, as a nurse to Mattie.

The negation, the blackness, in his [181/182] character is revealed also in his funereal satisfactions. When Mattie says she is not thinking of leaving be-

cause she has no place to go, "The answer sent a pang through him but the tone suffused him with joy." He rejoices in her helplessness; he is pained and thrilled at the same time because she has nowhere to go, because she too is trapped. Looking at the gravestones on his farm that have mocked him for years ("We never got away—how should you?"), he rejoices: ". . . all desire for change had vanished, and the sight of the little enclosure gave him a warm sense of continuance and stability."

"I guess we'll never let you go, Matt," he whispered, as though even the dead, lovers once, must conspire with him to keep her; and brushing by the graves, he thought: "We'll always go on living here together, and some day she'll lie there beside me."

The finest thought he can have is of the triangle going on forever, and then lying in the earth next to Mattie: "He was never so happy with her as when he abandoned himself to these dreams." Frome's aspirations do not finally go beyond darkness. His final acceptance of suicide is the culmination of his negative instincts: death is the blackest blackness.

III

Although the meaningful use of light and dark is pervasive in the book and is illuminating, it is the sexual symbolism that cuts deepest. The sexual symbolism is more dramatic than the two elements already discussed because it revolves around the key scenes in the book, Ethan and Mattie's night together and Zeena's return. It is also more significant because without an understanding of it the source of Zeena and Ethan's estrangement and antagonism remains unknown. After all, what *is* the deep gulf that lies between them? There is no explicit revelation in the book. In part, Wharton's use of symbolism to clarify the book's central problem is compatible with the inarticulateness of the characters. But perhaps also it represents a reticence or modesty of the

author's. Ethan and Mattie's night together is ostensibly a mild affair. Wharton might well have revealed then the
true relationship between Frome and his
wife and demonstrated overtly Mattie
and Ethan's transgression. But was it
really necessary for her to do so? Even as
it is, the evening progresses with the
greatest of intensity. Every action, every
word, even every silence quivers. It is because these apparently innocent actions
and words exist in such intensity that they
must be scrutinized. There are dispropor-
tions of feeling, particularly centering
around the pickle dish, that are revealing. A proper understanding of the
events of that evening sheds light
throughout the book, and particularly
makes the light and dark imagery more
meaningful.

Barrenness, infertility, is at the heart of
Frome's frozen woe. Not only is his farm
crippled, and finally his body too; his
sexuality is crippled also. Zeena, already
hypochondriac when he married her, has
had the effect of burying his manhood as
deeply as everything else in him. In seven
years of marriage there have been no
children. Within a year of their marriage,
Zeena developed her "sickliness." Medicine, sickness, and death are, in fact, rare-
ly out of sight in the book. The farm itself, with its separation of its vital center,
its regenerative center, suggests of course
the sexual repression. The name Starkfield also connotes barrenness. However,
Ethan and Zeena's sexual relationship is
suggested most by the incident of the
pickle dish, a dish which, unless understood, lies rather unaccountably at the
very center of the book.

The red pickle dish is Zeena's most
prized possession. She received it as a
[**182/183**] wedding gift. But she never
uses it. Instead she keeps it on a shelf,
hidden away. She takes it down only during spring cleaning, "and then I always
lifted it with my own hands, so's 't
shouldn't get broke." The dish has only
ceremonial, not functional, use. The sexual connotations here are obvious. The

fact that the wedding dish, which was
meant to contain pickles, in fact never
does, explains a lot of the heaviness of atmosphere, the chill, the frigidity. The
most intense scenes of the book, the most
revealing, center around this dish. For
example, Zeena never does discover an
affair in the making between Ethan and
Mattie, nor does she ever say anything,
except for one hint not followed up, that
reveals such knowledge. Her only discovery (and it is *the* discovery of the book)
is of her broken (and used) pickle dish.
It is this which brings the only tears to
her eyes in the entire book. When Zeena
is gone for a day, Mattie, significantly,
brings down and uses the pickle dish in
serving Ethan supper. Only if the dish is
properly understood can it be seen how
her violation is a sacrilege, as Zeena's
emotions amply testify. The dish is broken, and Ethan plans to glue it together.
Of course the dish can never be the same.
This kind of violation is irrevocable. Zeena does not discover that the dish is
broken until she gets, again significantly,
heartburn, the powders for which she
keeps on the same private shelf as the
pickle dish. The scene following is a symbolic recognition of the fact that Mattie
has usurped her place, broken her marriage, and become one with Ethan,
though in fact it was the cat (Zeena) who
actually broke the dish. The fact that
Zeena never truly filled her place, acted
the role of wife, and is herself responsible
for the failure of the marriage does not
bother her. Ethan is hers, however cere-
monially, and she resents what has happened. Her emotion transcends any literal meaning the dish may have, so much
so that other implications of the dish
force themselves on the reader. Speaking
to Mattie, she says,

". . . you waited till my back was turned, and
took the thing I set most store by of anything
I've got, and wouldn't never use it, not even
when the minister come to dinner, or Aunt Martha Pierce come over from Bettsbridge. . . . I
tried to keep my things where you couldn't get at
'em—and now you've took from me the one I

cared for most of all—" She broke off in a short spasm of sobs that passed and left her more than ever like the shape of a stone. . . . Gathering up the bits of broken glass she went out of the room as if she carried a dead body . . .

The passage reveals most clearly the gulf between Ethan and Zeena. The body she carries out is the corpse of her marriage. The evening that Mattie and Ethan spend together, then, is not as innocent as it seems on the surface. That Mattie and Ethan's infidelity is so indirectly presented, whether because of Wharton's sense of propriety or her desire to maintain a minimum of direct statement, does not at all lessen the reality of that fact. If the overt act of infidelity is not present, the emotional and symbolic act is. The passage is full of passion; the moment, for example, when Frome kisses the edge of the piece of material Mattie is holding has climactic intensity.

The sterility of their marriage, Frome's emasculation, is represented elsewhere. For example, just before Zeena leaves for the overnight trip to a doctor, she finishes a bottle of medicine and pushes it to Mattie: "It ain't done me a speck of good, but I guess I might as well use it up . . . If you can get the taste out it'll do for pickles." This is the only other mention of pickles in the book. Significantly, it is the last word in the chapter before the one devoted to Ethan and Mattie's night together. The action might be interpreted as follows: after Zeena has exhausted the possibilities of [**183/184**] her medicine for her "trouble," she turns to sex—but she passes on that alternative to Mattie. Mattie may use the jar for pickles if she wishes. The action is a foreshadowing of Mattie's use of the pickle dish. In a sense, Zeena has urged her to that act, for she is abdicating the position of sexual intiative.

Again, in *Ethan Frome* each word counts. But there are some descriptions, obviously very particular, that do not fit in with any generalizations already presented. However, in the light of an understanding of the pickle dish incident,

they are clarified. When Frome first points out his home, the narrator notes "the black wraith of a deciduous creeper" flapping on the porch. Deciduous means shedding leaves, or antlers, or horns, or teeth, at a particular season or stage of growth. Frome has indeed shed his manhood. Sexually he is in his winter season. Later, another vegetation is described on the porch: "A dead cucumber vine dangled from the porch like the crape streamer tied to the door for a death . . ." A cucumber is no more than a pickle. The pickle dish is not used; the cucumber vine is dead. That it should be connected with crape (black) and death is perfectly logical in the light of what has already been discussed about Frome. Frome's sexuality is dead. There is, of course, in all this the suggestion that Frome could revive if he could but reach spring, escape the winter of his soul. Mattie is his new season. At one point, where Mattie "shone" on him,

his soul swelled with pride as he saw how his tone subdued her. She did not even ask what he had done. Except when he was steering a big log down the mountain to his mill he had never known such a thrilling sense of mastery.

Mattie, as Zeena never does, makes Ethan feel the spring of his masculinity. But he never overcomes the ice of accumulated Starkfield winters. His final solution is to merge himself with winter forever.

Thus Ethan Frome, when he plunges towards what he considers certain death, is a failure but not a mystery. His behavior is not unmotivated; the tragedy is not contrived. The very heart of the novel is Frome's weakness of character, his negation of life. Behind that is his true, unfulfilled, relationship with Zeena. Wharton's economy of language in the novel is superb. There is hardly a word unnecessary to the total effect. Her final economy is the very brevity of the book. It fits the scene and character. There were depths to plumb; her people were not simple. To overcome the deficences of their natural reticence (and perhaps her own), to retain the strength of the severe and rugged setting, particularly the "outcropping granite," she resorted to a brilliant pattern of interlocking imagery and symbolism, three facets of which have been outlined here, to create a memorable work. The reader of *Ethan Frome*, then, need not find it merely a technically successful work, a virtuoso performance. With an understanding of the imagery and symbolism he can look into the heart of the book and see characters as full-bodied people in the grip of overwhelming emotional entanglements. He is also in a position to see the book's true dimensions as tragedy.

Ethan Frome: Structure and Metaphor*

JOSEPH X. BRENNAN (1924–   ) is an associate professor of English at the University of Notre Dame. Originally a student of Renaissance literature, he has in recent years published a number of articles on nineteenth-century and contemporary American fiction.

From the time of its first appearance in 1911 *Ethan Frome* has occupied a position in American letters as unique and strangely isolated as its tragic main character; because of the singular starkness of its theme and method, it has, in fact, even among the works of Edith Wharton, been long regarded as a "sport." In the considered opinion of Mrs. Wharton herself, it was the first of her works in which she "suddenly felt the artisan's full control of his implements";[1] but however pleased she may have been with her technical handling of the story, she always resented the common judgment that it was her best or most serious achievement. Among the general reading public, nevertheless, *Ethan Frome* has for decades been her chief—if not her only—claim to literary fame. Less unexpected but no less interesting have been the conflicting opinions of critics, for they have both extravagantly praised and vehemently condemned the work, and generally because of the same two features, its craft and characterization. John Crowe Ransom, for example, has found particular fault with its ingenious narrative framework, and both he and Alfred Kazin have severely remarked Mrs. Wharton's failure to comprehend the psychology of Ethan and his class.[2] E. K. Brown, on the other hand, though also unhappy about the narrative framework of the novel, has maintained that "de toutes les œuvres de Mrs. Wharton c'est celle qui a le plus de

chance de passer à la postérité. Il n'est pas d'œuvre de Henry James ou de William Dean Howells dont le sort soit plus assuré."[3] Percy Lubbock, moreover, has called this work "her classic," "a wonder of insight and divination";[4] and for Henry Seidel Canby it is no less than "a piece of perfect craftsmanship."[5] Though he refrains from naming this her best work, Blake Nevius, author of an authoritative full-length critical study of Mrs. Wharton's fiction, has nevertheless taken strong issue with the judgments of Ransom and [347/348] Kazin; and far from regarding it as a "sport," he has even characterized it as "her most indigenous work," belonging "to the main tradition of Mrs. Wharton's fiction," and having "a value, independent of its subject and technique, in helping us to define that tradition."[6]

In spite of the critical interest it has continually aroused, however, and the popularity it has from the first enjoyed, *Ethan Frome* has yet to receive the kind of detailed textual analysis many lesser works have long since enjoyed. To be sure, it has evoked a variety of commen-

---

[1] *A Backward Glance* (New York, 1934), p. 209.
[2] "Characters and Character," *American Review*, VI (Jan., 1936), pp. 271–288. *On Native Grounds* (New York, 1956), pp. 60–61.
[3] *Edith Wharton: Etude Critique* (Paris, 1935), p. 44.
[4] *Portrait of Edith Wharton* (New York, 1947), pp. 41, 242.
[5] *Literary History of the United States* (New York, 1953), p. 1211.
[6] *Edith Wharton* (Berkeley, 1953), pp. 24, 117–118.

* Joseph X. Brennan, "Ethan Frome: Structure and Metaphor," *Modern Fiction Studies*, VII (Winter, 1961–62), 347–356. Reprinted with the permission of the Purdue Research Foundation and the author.

tary, respecting its theme and narrative framework especially, but due attention has yet to be directed to its elaborate metaphorical patterns and the intricate relationship of those patterns to the narrator's sensibility. Only in a close study of these aspects of the novel, which determine its very tone and structure, can one begin to comprehend the reasons for its strange power and durability.

In her brief but illuminating introduction to *Ethan Frome* Mrs. Wharton directed the greater part of her attention to the narrator-framework of the novel, which she presumably regarded as her chief problem and special achievement. Whatever her real convictions may have been concerning her solution, John Crowe Ransom is certainly right in regarding the results as less than satisfactory. For the close reader readily discerns that the engineer-narrator did not really gather his story "bit by bit, from various people," but having been inspired by a few bare hints and scraps of information, created his "vision" of what *might* have been almost entirely out of the stuff of his vivid imagination. In short, the narrator who presents himself as an engineer in the realistic framework of the novel is actually a writer in disguise with the technical skill of a professional novelist and the sensibility of a poet; and his imaginative reconstruction of Ethan Frome's story, in view of what little he had to go by, is really no more than a brilliant fiction. Once one recognizes this fact, however, that we have to deal here with an overt fiction within a fiction, it is expedient, if not indeed necessary, to accept this arrangement as the very form of the novel and to analyze it as such. Hence the need for a close examination of the "vision" within the novel in relationship to its narrator as well as on its own terms.

From the many descriptions of the setting which one encounters in both the narrative framework and the "vision" of the novel, it is clear that the engineer-narrator is not only intensely responsive to the beauty of the natural scene and the seasons, but has a distinct predilection also for rendering his response in imagistic or poetic language. In the framework, for example, we encounter such "picture-making" passages as the following: [348/349]

When the storms of February had pitched their white tents about the devoted village and the wild cavalry of March winds had charged down to their support: I began to understand why Starkfield emerged from its six months' siege like a starved garrison capitulating without quarter. (p. 9) [7]

About a mile farther, on a road I had never travelled, we came to an orchard of starved appletrees writhing over a hillside among outcroppings of slate that nuzzled up through the snow like animals pushing out their noses to breathe. Beyond the orchard lay a field or two, their boundaries lost under the drifts; and above the fields, huddled against the white immensities of land and sky, one of those lonely New England farm-houses that make the landscape lonelier. (p. 21)

Even in his imaginative account of Ethan's history, the narrator frequently sets the scene with the same flair for metaphor:

Here and there a star pricked through, showing behind it a deep well of blue. In an hour or two the moon would push up over the ridge behind the farm, burn a gold-edged rent in the clouds, and then be swallowed by them. A mournful peace hung on the fields, as though they felt the relaxing grasp of the cold and stretched themselves in their long winter sleep. (p. 85)

Under the open sky the light was still clear, with a reflection of cold red on the eastern hills. The clumps of trees in the snow seemed to draw together in ruffled lumps, like birds with their heads under their wings; and the sky, as it paled, rose higher, leaving the earth more alone. (p. 169)

The narrator's acute sensitivity to the beauty of nature, in fact, accounts for much that is profoundly moving and memorable in *Ethan Frome,* so thoroughly does it permeate the whole novel, framework and vision alike.

[7] For my discussion of *Ethan Frome* I have used an edition copyrighted in 1922 by Charles Scribner's Sons.

It is not surprising, therefore, that in projecting the character of Ethan the narrator has liberally endowed him with much the same sensitivity he himself possesses. Though there is not the slightest indication from any source of evidence to which the engineer has access that either Ethan or Mattie was especially sensitive to the beauties of nature, the narrator has so thoroughly indued the two of them with this susceptibility that it both motivates and dominates their relationship; this becomes readily evident in the following key passage:

He had always been more sensitive than the people about him to the appeal of natural beauty. His unfinished studies had given form to this sensibility and even in his unhappiest moments field and sky spoke to him with a deep powerful persuasion. But hitherto the emotion had remained in him as a silent ache, veiling with sadness the beauty that evoked it. He did not even know whether any one else in the world felt as he did, or whether he was the sole victim of this mournful privilege. Then he learned that one other spirit had trembled with the same touch of wonder: that at his side, living under his roof and eating his [**349/350**] bread, was a creature to whom he could say: "That's Orion down yonder; the big fellow to the right is Aldebaran, and the bunch of little ones—like bees swarming—they're the Pleiades. . . ." . . . And there were other sensations, less definable but more exquisite, which drew them together with a shock of silent joy: the cold red of sunset behind winter hills, the flight of cloudflocks over slopes of golden stubble, or the intensely blue shadows of hemlocks on sunlit snow. When she said to him once: "It looks just as if it was painted!" it seemed to Ethan that the art of definition could go no farther, and that words had at last been found to utter his secret soul. (pp. 36–38)

This special sensitivity, shared equally by the narrator and his imagined characters, accounts, moreover, for the many skeins of imagery which pattern the envisioned story. It accounts, first of all, for the chief pattern of contrast which runs throughout this story, that between indoors and outdoors, between the house as the symbolic stronghold of moral convention and conformity, and the open countryside as symbolic of natural freedom and passional abandon. And it accounts

also for the elaborate system of metaphorical characterization developed in direct relationship to this basic symbolic pattern.

Of the many natural objects and locations which constitute the pattern of outdoor imagery, the two black Norway spruces are surely the most important, since they provide the setting for the lovers' uttermost passion and final fatal resolve. In their symbolical dark shadows, indeed, the story of Ethan and Mattie's secret passion virtually begins and ends. When for the first time in Chapter II they stand together in this darkness, their deep mutual passion is no less intense, and all the more painful, for being unexpressed and forbidden:

He slipped an arm through hers . . . and fancied it was faintly pressed against her side; but neither of them moved. It was so dark under the spruces that he could barely see the shape of her head beside his shoulder. He longed to stoop his cheek and rub it against her scarf. He would have liked to stand there with her all night in the blackness. (p. 49)

In Chapter IX, when they again stand together under these spruces, they give passionate avowal to that love, of which, but three nights earlier, there had been only mute intimations. And it is in this darkness, finally, a darkness now of utter hopelessness, that they resolve to die together. Thus the spruces both shelter their forbidden love and foreshadow its tragic ending, forming a kind of dark parentheses to the brief interlude of their passion.

In direct antithesis to the dark freedom which the out-of-doors provides is the atmosphere of moral restriction which pervades the lamplit kitchen. When Ethan mentioned to Mattie the next evening, as they sat together in the kitchen, that he had seen a friend of hers getting [**350/351**] kissed under the Varnum spruces, Mattie "blushed to the roots of her hair" and replied "in a low voice, as though he had suddenly touched on something grave." The paragraph following upon this passage points up sharply the contrary psychological and symbolic implications of these contrasting locations.

Ethan had imagined that his allusion might open the way to the accepted pleasantries, and these perhaps in turn to a harmless caress, if only a mere touch on her hand. But now he felt as if her blush had set a flaming guard about her. . . . He knew that most young men made nothing at all of giving a pretty girl a kiss, and he remembered that the night before, when he had put his arm about Mattie, she had not resisted. But that had been out-of-doors, under the open irresponsible night. Now, in the warm lamplit room, with all its ancient implications of conformity and order, she seemed infinitely farther away from him and more unapproachable. (p. 100)

Insofar as the narrator has imagined and set these scenes, this symbolic use of the Norway spruces directly reflects his informing sensibility. The characterization of Mattie and Zeena, however, though ultimately derived from the narrator's sensibility also, nevertheless becomes the immediate responsibility of Ethan in the envisioned story, for it is through his sensibility and from his point of view that this vision is projected. The distinction, of course, is a logical rather than real one, since the two sensibilities are really only one.

The imagistic light in which both Mattie and Zeena are consistently regarded by Ethan, in any event, is directly related to this larger pattern of contrast. In Ethan's mind, it is interesting to note, Mattie is constantly associated with the most lovely and delicate objects in nature. Her face "always looked like a window that has caught the sunset"; "it was part of the sun's red and of the pure glitter of the snow"; and it "changed with each turn of their talk, like a wheat-field under a summer breeze." Noteworthy also are the descriptions of Mattie's hair. Seen from behind, as she carried a lamp before her, it looked to Ethan "like a drift of mist on the moon"; and while she washed the dishes, the steam tightened "her rough hair into little brown rings like the tendrils of the traveller's joy."

To the touch of his lips, moreover, Ethan found that her hair was "soft yet springy, like certain mosses on warm slopes, and had the faint woody fragrance of fresh sawdust in the sun"; and later, "he looked at her hair and longed to touch it again, and to tell her that it smelt of the woods." In the most passionate scene under the spruces, finally, Ethan stroked her hair, wanting "to get the feeling of it into his hand, so that it would sleep there like a seed in winter."

Especially important, and even symbolic, is the frequent association of Mattie with birds: for Ethan, "the motions of her mind were as incalculable as the flit of a bird in the branches"; and "her hands **[351/352]** went up and down above the strip of stuff, just as he had seen a pair of birds make short perpendicular flights over a nest they were building." To him, also, her voice was a "sweet treble," and "the call of a bird in a mountain ash was so like her laughter that his heart tightened and then grew large." Of particular interest, therefore, is the manner in which, after the smash-up, Mattie's whimpering is confused in Ethan's mind with the sound of both a bird and a field-mouse: "The stillness was so profound that he heard a little animal twittering somewhere nearby under the snow. It made a small frightened *cheep* like a field mouse. . . ." Since Zeena, as we shall see below, is consistently associated with and even identified by her cat, this shift from the image of the small bird, the eternal but more elusive quarry of cats, to that of the field mouse, their more defenseless prey, is obviously symbolic of Zeena's final victory over Mattie.

Reinforcing these principal associations of Mattie with nature are a number of related but subordinate images. During a summer picnic, for example, Mattie looked as "bright as a blackberry" to Ethan as she attended a "gipsy fire." Elsewhere in the novel, when she learned from Ethan that she was to be dismissed, she stood silent, "drooping before him like a broken branch"; and as they embraced shortly thereafter, he felt "her lashes beat his cheek like netted butterflies."

Into the characterization of Mattie, furthermore, the narrator has quite deliberately woven a streak of symbolic red; she is so frequently connected with this color, in fact, that by the end of the story her personality is vividly imbued with the passion, vibrancy, and daring nonconformity which red traditionally connotes. In the opening scene, for example, she is imagined wearing a "cherry-coloured 'fascinator,'" with "the colour of the cherry scarf in her fresh lips and cheeks"; and in anticipation of her night alone with Ethan, "through her hair she had run a streak of crimson ribbon." Later that evening "her cheeks burned redder" and she "blushed to the roots of her hair," setting "a flaming guard about her." Of particular import in this scene, moreover, is the "dish of gay red glass" which Mattie had taken down from the forbidden shelf of Zeena's special possessions. As an object of beauty and gaiety, which Zeena, significantly, had never used once since her wedding, this gay red dish suggests symbolically the pleasure and passion that Ethan had sought and Zeena had thwarted in their marriage. As Zeena's property by marriage and by right, it represents also, respecting Ethan and Mattie, a forbidden pleasure and illicit passion. The shattering of the red dish, moreover, clearly prefigures the final shattering of their limbs and ill-starred love.

In direct contrast to this rendering of Mattie in terms of nature and vibrant reds, are the descriptions of Zeena suggesting the arti-[352/353]ficial, angular, and unhealthy. This contrast is brought into sharpest focus in the following paralleled passages, in which, on successive evenings, first Zeena and then Mattie let Ethan in at the back door:

Against the dark background of the kitchen she stood up tall and angular, one hand drawing a quilted counterpane to her flat breast, while the other held a lamp. The light, on a level with her chin, drew out of the darkness her puckered throat and the projecting wrist of the hand that clutched the quilt, and deepened fantastically the hollows and prominences of her high-boned face under its ring of crimping-pins. . . .

She drew aside without speaking, and Mattie and Ethan passed into the kitchen, which had the deadly chill of a vault after the dry cold of the night. (p. 58)

She stood just as Zeena had stood, a lifted lamp in her hand, against the black background of the kitchen. She held the light at the same level, and it drew out with the same distinctness her slim young throat and the brown wrist no bigger than a child's. Then, striking upward, it threw a lustrous fleck on her lips, edged her eyes with velvet shade, and laid a milky whiteness above the black curve of her brows.

She wore her usual dress of darkish stuff, and there was no bow at her neck; but through her hair she had run a streak of crimson ribbon. This tribute to the unusual transformed and glorified her. She seemed to Ethan taller, fuller, more womanly in shape and motion. She stood aside, smiling silently, while he entered and then moved away from him with something soft and flowing in her gait. . . . A bright fire glowed in the stove. . . . (pp. 87–88)

In contrast to Mattie's vivid coloring and beauty, Zeena's face was "drawn and bloodless," "grayish," and "sallow," with "fretful" "querulous lines"; her hair was "thin," her lips "straight," her eyes "lashless," and her looks "queer." At table she made a "familiar gesture of adjusting her false teeth before she began to eat," and she "always went to bed as soon as she had her supper." Before going to bed, however, she wrapped her head "in a piece of yellow flannel"; and then she slept, breathing asthmatically, "her mouth slightly open, her false teeth in a tumbler by the bed. . . ." In short, "she was already an old woman."

Countering the metaphorical association of Mattie and birds, moreover, is the more literal and obvious relationship between Zenobia and her cat. In the long anticipated evening of Zeena's absence, in fact, the cat directly becomes her watchful surrogate: "The cat jumped into Zeena's chair . . . and lay watching them with narrowed eyes." Subsequently the cat creates the illusion of Zeena's presence rather eerily when it "jumped from Zeena's chair to dart at a mouse," setting the empty chair to a "spectral rocking." Earlier in the evening the cat had disrupted their happiness even more violently by breaking the red pickle-dish, the symbol of their forbidden passion. In its cunning, cruelty, and languid domesticity the cat indeed is the perfect representative of its mistress. It seems, too, that the stuffed owl in the parlor was introduced to further suggest Zeena's affinity for the [353/354] artificial and predaceous. In any event nothing natural and beautiful seems to thrive in her domain of drugs and patent medicines; even the kitchen geraniums fade and "pine away." From the characterization of Zeena in both the narrative framework and the story proper, moreover, one is evidently intended to infer that she gathers a certain morbid strength from the weakness and illness of others: vulture-like she diligently attends the dying.

In close connection with this pattern of contrasts in the characterizations of Zeena and Mattie, there appears another set of contrasts in which Ethan himself figures. At the beginning of the novel, when the narrator first beholds Ethan, twenty-four years after his smash-up, the things which most impress him are his deep taciturnity and moral isolation, traits for which the frozen landscape most aptly suggests the verbal formulations:

He seemed a part of the mute melancholy landscape, an incarnation of its frozen woe, with all that was warm and sentient in him fast bound below the surface. . . . I simply felt that he lived in a depth of moral isolation too remote for casual access, and I had the sense that his loneliness . . . had in it . . . the profound accumulated cold of many Starkfield winters. (pp. 15–16)

It is interesting to note, therefore, that as the narrator envisions Ethan's relationship with Mattie, twenty-four years earlier, "she, the quicker, finer, more expressive, instead of crushing him by the contrast, had given him something of her own ease and freedom." And since she is most frequently associated with summer

imagery, it is not surprising that as they make their way home the first evening, Ethan's growing conviction of their mutual love is paralleled by an imagistic progression from spring thaw to summer warmth and flow:

Her wonder and his laughter ran together like spring rills in a thaw. (p. 49)

The iron heavens seemed to melt and rain down sweetness. (p. 53)

They walked on as if they were floating on a summer stream. (p. 56)

The joyful anticipation of spending the evening alone with Mattie further unlocks Ethan from his wintry taciturnity: "he, who was usually so silent, whistled and sang aloud as he drove through the snowy fields. There was in him a slumbering spark of sociability which the long Starkfield winters had not yet extinguished" (p. 73). And sitting in the kitchen with Mattie that night, "he had a confused sense of being in another world, where all was warmth and harmony . . . ," so that, finally, "all constraint had vanished between the two, and they began to talk easily and simply." In their most passionate embrace two nights later under the Varnum spruces, this progression from wintry cold to summer heat reaches its culmination: "once he found her mouth again, and they seemed to be by the pond [354/355] together in the burning August sun." The summer of their love, nevertheless, was destined from the first to be only a short one, to be almost the illusion of one: "all their intercourse had been made up of just such inarticulate flashes, when they seemed to come suddenly upon happiness as if they had surprised a butterfly in the winter woods."

In opposition to the imagistic warmth and ease characterizing his relationship with Mattie is the chill, numbness, and paralysis which typifies his relationship with his wife. Ironically it was Ethan's very dread of loneliness, silence, and isolation—all symbolically related to winter—that had induced him to marry Zee-na in the first place. Before long, how-ever, he became increasingly aware of Zeena's real nature, of her hypochondria, her "narrow-mindedness and ignorance." "Then she too fell silent"; and recalling his mother's growing taciturnity, Ethan began to wonder if Zeena were also turn-ing "queer." "At times, looking at Zee-na's shut face, he felt the chill of such forebodings." By the time of Mattie's ar-rival, nevertheless, the estrangement of the couple was so complete that even with his love for Mattie suffusing his whole being, the mere mention of her name was sufficient to seal him in silence: "Ethan, a moment earlier, had felt himself on the brink of eloquence; but the mention of Zeena had paralyzed him."

Just as the house stands in symbolic opposition to the out-of-doors, so too the bedroom of Zeena and Ethan is the direct symbolic counterpart of the shadows of the Norway spruces. For at the end of Chapter II and the beginning of Chapter III, it is evident that the bedroom repre-sents for Ethan his suffocating marital commitment to Zeena and his frustrating separation from Mattie. The bedroom, moreover, is the scene of the first incident "of open anger between the couple in their sad seven years together"; in this scene, the obvious antithesis to that of the lovers under the spruces, "their thoughts seemed to dart at each other like serpents shooting venom." Thus Ethan's desertion of his bed that same night and his retirement to the study be-low foreshadow his subsequent resolution to desert Zeena and run away with Mat-tie.

Ethan's hope of an escape from his bondage to Zeena, however, soon withers in the harsh light of day and reality: "The inexorable facts closed in on him like prison-warders handcuffing a convict. There was no way out—none. He was a prisoner for life. . . ." Returning now to the narrative framework, one notes that this image of the shackles reappears in

the description of Ethan's lameness "checking each step like the jerk of a chain." His very attempt to escape through suicide, in fact, had only dou-bled the bonds of his captivity; for his crippled body only objectifies the warped state of his soul, now chained [355/356] to the ruins of a tragic marriage and even more tragic love. It is no wonder, then, that Ethan appears to the engineer to be already "dead" and "in hell." Here there is no hope or meaningfulness at all—only the endurance of despair.

In retrospect it may be seen more clear-ly how intricately *Ethan Frome* is struc-tured. In spite of the obvious formal dis-tinction between the framework and the narrator's "vision," the two parts are nev-ertheless complexly interrelated; the ac-count of Ethan's tragic love, in fact, is so thoroughly informed by the sensibility and imagination of its narrator that the story can be adequately analyzed only in terms of that relationship. Since the narrator has had to imagine almost the whole of Ethan's history and the most important traits of his character as well, in many respects, inevitably, the sensibil-ities of the two are indistinguishable.

It seems to me, therefore, that it would be much more reasonable to judge the novel in terms of the special character of the narrator's mind—his predilection for poetic, symbolic design and an abstract ideal of human nature—rather than in terms of psychological realism. For even within the formal structure and state-ment of the work, Ethan and Mattie and Zeena are much more imagined than real characters. One may take issue, perhaps, with the rightness of the narrator's vision but certainly not with his right—or the right of the author—to imagine it as his peculiar sensibility dictates. Respecting this "vision," finally, and its metaphori-cal construction, it may be well to recall what Henry James wrote in defense of *Daisy Miller*, that his "supposedly typical little figure was of course pure poetry, and had never been anything else."

Suggested Topics for Controlled Research

In addition to the text of *Ethan Frome,* the materials in this anthology are of two kinds: (1) Edith Wharton's own comments on the genesis and reception of her novel, and (2) critical appraisals of the novel as a whole or some aspect of it, spanning half a century and representing a wide spectrum of evaluation.

It is important of course that you read Mrs. Wharton's story and ask yourself certain questions about its method before allowing your response to the work to be modified by what others have said about it. The first and most obvious of these questions involves the point of view. Why did Mrs. Wharton find it necessary to surround her story proper with a framework narrative utilizing a visitor to Starkfield who conveys to us his "vision" of the events of a quarter of a century ago? Could the story have been told as effectively, or more effectively, without this device? Was her selection of a framework narrator a good one? Or, to phrase the question more narrowly, does Mrs. Wharton make it seem plausible that such an individual as her narrator would be able to get to the bottom of Ethan's story?

Since the events of the story are not presented in a strict chronological sequence it might be useful to diagram the time-scheme of the novel before proceeding to ask other questions about plot, characterization, and setting. When you have done so you will better be able to inquire whether Mrs. Wharton has told us at any given juncture in the narrative all we need to know—about the characters, their histories, and their present circumstances—or why she has seen fit to delay revealing certain information. What, in fact, *do* we need to know about the three main characters to make their

fate seem plausible? Has Mrs. Wharton told us too little? too much? For if the action of the novel is to be tested in terms of what we know about the characters, there must be a careful adjustment of cause and effect. It is a matter of artistic economy: we need know only so much as will explain the fate of the characters, no more and no less. Two specific questions may help clarify this problem. Is Ethan's and Mattie's suicide attempt adequately motivated? Has Mrs. Wharton exhausted all the alternatives for the lovers—the alternatives, at least, that square with their characters and circumstances?

For nearly two centuries the novel has shown a progressive awareness of the relation between character and environment. We reflect places; places reflect us. Setting may be used in the novel as a mirror of inner reality, a projection of the characters' traits, ideas, and feelings, conscious or unconscious, and of their situation or circumstances; conversely, the characters may embody, in their appearance, speech, gestures, and motives, certain aspects of their environment. In *Ethan Frome* this imaginative interdependence of character and milieu is conveyed through an insistent and for the most part subtle use of imagery and symbolism. Before reading Kenneth Bernard's and Joseph X. Brennan's elaborate analyses of this technique you should see how far your own awareness will carry you, particularly since these two essays exhibit not only a difference of emphasis but occasional differences of interpretation (e.g., in defining the symbolic value of Zeena's pickle-dish) . Finally, one of the frequent criticisms of American local-color fiction has been that it fails to make the leap, as it were, from the particular to the universal. You may want to consider whether the action of *Ethan Frome* could have taken place outside its New England setting or whether it is bound up inextricably with the elements present in a particular milieu.

Among the documents in the second section of this anthology is an early version of the "enveloping" or framework narrative of *Ethan Frome,* transcribed from the fragmentary manuscript at Yale University. In reproducing it I have omitted the many variant readings in the manuscript in favor of providing the version which represents Mrs. Wharton's clear intentions at this stage in the composition of the story. The manuscript version differs significantly from the final published version. In comparing the two you should first of all consider Mrs. Wharton's additions to the final version. Why, so far as one can infer, did she find them necessary? Second, you should examine the changes in diction between the early version and the final version. In what way do they modify our impression of the characters (Ethan and the narrator), the relationship between them, and the tone of the narrative (that is, the narrator's attitude toward his material)?

The body of serious criticism on *Ethan Frome* is not large, and much of what does exist is skeptical in tone. Aside from Lionel Trilling's attack on the story because it produces no "moral reverberations," most of the criticism (as well as Mrs. Wharton's rejoinders) centers on two questions: (1) whether Edith Wharton really knew the segment of New England life she was portraying or whether she betrayed the uncertainty of the "outsider," and (2) whether the way she chose to tell the story was, as she claimed, "justified in the given case" or was, as John Crowe Ransom suggests, an elaborate evasion. Today it may not be very profitable to debate the first question. Even those who claim the special authority conferred by having grown up in New England around the turn of the century

cannot agree. Elizabeth Shepley Sergeant ("Idealized New England") says of Mrs. Wharton's characters, setting, and drama that "in spite of the *vraisemblance,* she has got them all wrong." Owen Davis, co-author of the dramatic version of *Ethan Frome,* born in just such a village as "Starkfield" in northern Maine and having grown up, as he claims, among just such characters as Mrs. Wharton portrayed, insists that "Edith Wharton has I think written of them more brilliantly than any other writer has ever done or can ever hope to do." [1] But since this is a game anyone can play, even a southerner, John Crowe Ransom, imagines that he knows Ethan "better than Mrs. Wharton does," and Bernard De Voto, a transplanted westerner, can assert that "Mrs. Wharton's New England was a seasonal landscape through which one drove with Henry James."

Nevertheless, there *are* signs in *Ethan Frome* that Mrs. Wharton had difficulty in establishing her credentials. Only after you have considered for yourself her choice of point of view—her solution to *how* the story was to be told—should you read her own defense of her choice in Part Two of this anthology and then follow the debate over the question in Part Three. Basically, the question resolves itself into a single issue: Was it necessary to introduce an intermediary between Mrs. Wharton and her readers, a character who would function as narrator—what she called "a sympathizing intermediary between [the author's] rudimentary characters and the more complicated minds to whom he is trying to present them"? Could not the author herself serve this function, as in effect Edith Wharton does in the story proper as opposed to the framework story? In other words, why did Mrs. Wharton reject the possibility, among others, of telling the story directly, in her own voice (as she did in *Summer,* her other story of New England life), and is it fair to say that

[1] "Change But Not Decline," New York *Times,* February 2, 1936, Section 9, p. 1.

the sole *raison d'être* of the intermediary, as has sometimes been suggested, was the author's desire to extract the maximum effect from her closing episode, that tableau of defeat in the farmhouse kitchen? In pursuing this topic it will be helpful to read the extract from Mrs. Wharton's *The Writing of Fiction,* where although she is talking about the short story her remarks apply with equal validity to what she called "the *long* short-story," such as *Ethan Frome.*

Before reading very far into the criticism of *Ethan Frome* you will be aware of the extent to which certain clichés have taken hold. Some critics repeat the prejudices, casual or informed, of other critics; others make the act of criticism an occasion to impose their own views and in the process distort the intrinsic meanings of the work. One way to understand what Mrs. Wharton was trying to do in *Ethan Frome* is to understand, with the unintentional help of such criticism, what she was not trying to do. It does a gross injustice to the story, for example,

to declare as a socialist critic once did that it was to him "above all else a judgment on that system which fails to redeem such villages as Mrs. Wharton's Starkfield." [2] Such an interpretation stems, not from the work itself, but from the critic's moral and ideological preoccupations. Taking either a single essay on *Ethan Frome* (such as Lionel Trilling's "The Morality of Inertia" or Bernard De Voto's Introduction to the 1938 reissue of the novel) or a group of essays, ask yourself what assumptions—whether about the nature of literature, its aims, and its techniques, or about, for example, society or ethics or psychology—determine the individual critic's interpretation of the story. Such an exercise may help clear the ground for what is badly needed: a reappraisal of *Ethan Frome* that does not begin as well as end with the contradictory notion that it is a seriously flawed classic.

[2] Edwin Björkman, "The Greater Edith Wharton," *Voices of Tomorrow* (New York: Mitchell Kennerley, 1913), p. 297.

Suggested Topics for Library Research

A number of research topics utilizing in part the materials in this volume will be suggested below. Others may suggest themselves to you as you read the documents; still others as you become acquainted with the books, articles, and primary sources available in the library.

There is no comprehensive bibliography of Edith Wharton's writings. A checklist of her works may be found in Blake Nevius, *Edith Wharton* (Berkeley and Los Angeles, 1953), pp. 260–263. For articles about her, consult Lewis Leary, ed., *Articles on American Literature, 1900–1950* (Durham, N.C., 1954); the selective bibliography in Nevius, pp. 264–265; and, as a supplement to these, for the period after 1950, the quarterly bibliographies in the journal *American Literature*. To be recommended are Irving Howe, ed., *Edith Wharton: A Collection of Critical Essays* (Englewood Cliffs, N.J., 1962) and the brief survey of Mrs. Wharton's achievement in Louis Auchincloss, *Edith Wharton* (Minneapolis, 1961).

Similarly, there is no adequate biography of Edith Wharton. This is largely because her papers, in the Collection of American Literature at Yale University, will not be opened to scholars until 1968. There are, however, a number of sources of biographical information: Mrs. Wharton's discreet memoir, *A Backward Glance* (New York, 1934); Percy Lubbock's *Portrait of Edith Wharton* (New York, 1947), a minor classic of biographical writing, though as reticent in important matters as Mrs. Wharton's autobiography and rather weak on the novelist's early career; the Introduction to Wayne Andrews' *The Best Short Stories of Edith Wharton* (New York, 1958), which bears the subtitle "Fragment of A Biography in Progress"; and, most recently, Millicent Bell's *Edith Wharton and Henry James* (New York, 1965), a detailed and richly informative record of that notable friendship.

If you are interested in the genesis of *Ethan Frome* and can read French, you may want to examine W. D. MacCallan's "The French Draft of *Ethan Frome*," *Yale University Library Gazette,* XXII (July, 1952), 38–47, which reprints the earliest version of the story, undertaken as an exercise in French. (It was not lost, as Mrs. Wharton asserts in both "The Writing of *Ethan Frome*" and *A Backward Glance*). Mr. MacCallan's commentary on the differences between this version and the final one is minimal. A more thorough and searching comparison would make an interesting paper. Further insight into Mrs. Wharton's intentions in *Ethan Frome* may be obtained by comparing the method of that story with that of two other, related stories: Honoré de Balzac's "La Grande Bretêche" (the Library Edition of *The Novels of Balzac*, Vol. 12, Philadelphia, 1898), which Edith Wharton cited as a precedent for her "method" in *Ethan Frome,* and Mrs. Wharton's "The Duchess at Prayer," in *Crucial Instances* (New York, 1901), which, unlike *Ethan Frome,* is a strikingly literal adaptation of Balzac's story. The comparison may suggest, incidentally, the ultimate source of Mrs. Wharton's much-debated conclusion to *Ethan Frome.*

A more comprehensive subject is the relation of Edith Wharton's tale to the whole body of New England local-color fiction which, beginning with Harriet Beecher Stowe's *Oldtown Folks* (1869), reached its efflorescence in the 1880's and produced, among other distinguished fiction, that of Sarah Orne Jewett and Mary Wilkins Freeman. Beyond that is the question of *Ethan Frome*'s relation to the local-color fiction of other regions, such as Hamlin Garland's *Main-Travelled Roads* (1891) or Sherwood Anderson's *Winesburg, Ohio* (1919), which transcends the genre in a way that few of its predecessors do. (A useful introduction to local-color writing is Claude Simpson's anthology *The Local Colorists* [New York, 1960]). Even though it is difficult, at this distance in time, to scout Mrs. Wharton's contention that Miss Jewett and Mrs. Freeman viewed their New England through "rose-coloured spectacles," it would be rewarding to compare *Ethan Frome* with the best work of her rivals: Miss Jewett's *Deephaven* (1877) and *The Country of the Pointed Firs* (1896) and Mrs. Freeman's *A Humble Romance* (1887) and *A New England Nun* (1891). Elizabeth Shepley Sergeant's essay "Idealized New England," reprinted in this collection, ranges itself on the side of the earlier generation of New England local colorists. As she admits, her position was taken mainly in reaction to the view expressed in an essay, "Mrs. Wharton's World," by the novelist Robert Herrick (1868–1938), published in the *New Republic*, II (February 13, 1915), 40–42. Herrick argued that *Ethan Frome* is superior to Mrs. Wharton's earlier novels, those which dealt with a world she knew intimately, precisely *because* its characters and their way of life were beyond her immediate ken. Between them Miss Sergeant and Herrick have raised an important theoretical question which seeks to determine the relative importance of the observed fact and the plastic imagination. It is a question that their discussions pursue only a short distance, however, and consequently one that you might profitably attempt to define and resolve for yourself. A useful contribution to the debate will be found in Henry James's well known essay "The Art of Fiction" and, to a lesser degree, in his "The Life of George Eliot," both of which appear in his *Partial Portraits* (1888).

In the Introduction I spoke in passing of *Ethan Frome*'s relation to the main body of Mrs. Wharton's fiction. A study of this relation might begin with that other chronicle of pinched, defeated lives, "Bunner Sisters" (1916), and with Mrs. Wharton's second and possibly, as some readers feel, superior novel of New England life, *Summer* (1917). Other novels that bear interesting thematic resemblances to *Ethan Frome,* however far removed in their characters and settings, are the major works, *The House of Mirth* (1905), *The Custom of the Country* (1913), and *The Age of Innocence* (1920). All, it might be remarked in the most general sense, are concerned with what George Eliot once defined as "the great problem of the shifting relation between passion and duty," a theme which was of particular interest to Edith Wharton because of its relevance to her personal dilemma. One of Mrs. Wharton's most revealing formulations of this theme is in her review of Leslie Stephens' *George Eliot,* in *The Bookman,* XV (May 1902), 247–251.

An especially challenging and useful project for you to undertake is a comparison of Mrs. Wharton's story with the dramatic version by Owen and Donald Davis which appeared on Broadway in the late winter and spring of 1936 and was published soon after as *Ethan Frome: A Dramatization of Edith Wharton's Novel* (New York, 1936). The comparison would have to take into account, first of all, the different *means* available to the novelist and the dramatist. The medium of the story is words; the medium of the drama is the theatre. Narrative, as a recent book puts it, is distinguished by "the presence of a story and a story-teller," whereas "a drama is a story without a story-teller."[1] In reading the story we depend on the reliability of the

---

[1] Robert Scholes and Robert Kellogg, *The Nature of Narrative* (New York: Oxford University Press, 1966), p. 4.

narrator, though we are not only permitted but are obligated to look beyond his individual view of the events, to ask ourselves if it is too narrowly conditioned, and to modify it if necessary in the interests of a reality that we believe to be larger than his particular vision. In viewing a drama—at least a conventionally realistic drama like the Davises' version of *Ethan Frome*—we are less conscious of the interposition of a personal view of life, for the dramatist is not present to comment or interpret. The inner lives of his characters can be revealed only through what they say or do, though these means may be enhanced by the contribution of the theatre—that is, of the director, stage designer, lighting technician—a contribution that the imaginative reader of the script will have to make for himself. It is apparent too that the dramatist is compelled by his medium to handle exposition in a different way. In the story it may be presented directly by the narrator or indirectly through the thoughts as well as speech of the characters. In the drama it is more difficult to accomplish this naturally and unobtrusively because everything must be conveyed to us through dialogue.

An essay on the narrative and dramatic versions of *Ethan Frome* might therefore begin with a consideration of the different expressive means of the narrative and the drama and the problems they entail (a question barely opened in the last paragraph) and then proceed to specific questions about the dramatists' modifications of Mrs. Wharton's story. Are their alterations justifiable, that is, are they compelled by the dramatic or theatrical medium? Do they violate Mrs. Wharton's intentions in her story (if in no other way, by putting essentially inarticulate characters on the stage)? How would you defend the dramatists' practice of transposing incidents in the story's chronology (e.g., the pickle-dish episode) or motives from one character to another (compare, for example, Chapter VIII of the story with Act II, scene 2, of the play)? Consider also whether, in the transfer of the story to the stage, there has been any loss in the complexity of motives which the main characters project and consequently in the complexity of their individual dilemmas. The roles of certain characters in Mrs. Wharton's story have been eliminated or diminished or enlarged. Is there any necessity for retaining the narrator (designated only as "The Young Man") in the play? And why do the dramatists find it necessary to enhance Jotham's role? Finally, in answering these and other questions you might keep in mind a more general question: Is the dramatists' treatment of the story superior in any respects to Mrs. Wharton's? Or, to put it another way, do the problems they were forced to solve and the solutions they achieved point to any defects in Mrs. Wharton's original conception?